# THE NATURE AND
# CHEMISTRY OF HIGH POLYMERS

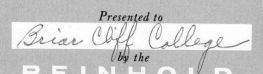

"MAY ALL THE CURSES of the good Bishop Ernulphus light on the borrower-and-not-returner or upon the stealer of this book."

(Sir William Osler's inscription on the fly-leaf of his own copy of his *Textbook on the Principles and Practice of Medicine*)

# Selected Topics in Modern Chemistry

## SERIES EDITORS

*Professor Harry H. Sisler*
*University of Florida*
*Gainesville, Florida*

*Professor Calvin A. VanderWerf*
*Hope College*
*Holland, Michigan*

AMONG THE most exciting areas of current research is the study of giant molecules, particularly those which have been formed in the laboratory or manufacturing plant according to predetermined sets of specifications. The principles which guide the chemist in building such molecules and which thus enable the chemist to function as a "molecular architect" constitute a major portion of this new addition to the SELECTED TOPICS IN MODERN CHEMISTRY Series. We are fortunate indeed to have as the author of this volume a chemist with demonstrated ability in research in polymer chemistry and an outstanding reputation as a dynamic and effective teacher in the field of polymer science. The student will find this volume most helpful not only in his studies in chemistry but in the many corollary fields where the study of large molecules plays an important role.

HARRY H. SISLER
CALVIN A. VANDERWERF

# THE NATURE AND CHEMISTRY OF HIGH POLYMERS

KENNETH F. O'DRISCOLL

*Associate Professor of Chemistry*
*Villanova University*
*Villanova, Pennsylvania*

New York
REINHOLD PUBLISHING CORPORATION
Chapman & Hall, Ltd., London

# PREFACE

As a subject for academic discussion and formal course work, the chemistry of high polymers is relatively neglected. Most chemists complete their undergraduate training with little more than a lecture or two on polymers in their organic course and a discussion of colloids in physical chemistry. In graduate school a small percentage of the students take a survey course in polymer chemistry. Some, of course, do their graduate research in the polymer area, but the number is quite small. Yet it is safe to estimate, in spite of the paucity of polymer training given to them, that more than half of the chemists today will be engaged in working with polymers at one time or another. This book is addressed to those chemists, student or graduate, who may be interested in polymers, but have not had formal training in the subject.

The number of books fit for use in a graduate level course in polymer chemistry grows yearly. This book will not provide any competition for them. Rather, it is intended to serve as an introduction to them for a person seriously intent on learning about polymers *or* to provide a background for the chemist who would like to know "less than all" about an important topic. As such, it requires no more than a slight acquaintance with organic chemistry and chemical bond formation.

Detailed references to specific journal articles and books have not been given in the text, for it is my opinion that such references are usually ignored by the reader seeking only an introduction to the topic. In their place, I offer an annotated bibliography, incomplete but reflecting my own prejudices on good books for further information. The writing of this book would have been far more difficult without their existence. Even more important, though, have been the training and direction originally given me by Professor Arthur Tobolsky, one of the very few polymer chemists whose research has ranged over the entire field, from organic polymerizations to polymer physics.

It is also a pleasure to acknowledge invaluable help from Professors William Barnhurst, Thomas Doyne, and Dominic Roberti, of Villanova University, and George Butler and Harry Sisler, of the University of Florida, for their readings of all or parts of the manuscript.

KENNETH F. O'DRISCOLL

*Villanova, Pennsylvania*
*May, 1964*

# CONTENTS

# THE NATURE AND
# CHEMISTRY OF HIGH POLYMERS

# NATURE OF
# HIGH· POLYMERS

MANY EONS AGO, at a time too distant to be fully comprehended by man, a living organism reproduced itself for the first time. Scarcely more than 100 years ago a French chemist named Simon observed that an oily organic liquid, called styrene, could be converted to a gelatinous, almost solid mass by heating or prolonged standing. These two events, widely separated in time and character, had a most significant common feature. The organism in its reproduction produced a *protein*; the chemist in his laboratory produced polystyrene. Both of these substances are *polymers*. The protein was the result of forces behaving as dictated by the nature of the organism. The polystyrene was also the result of natural forces, but these were given their impetus by the chemist's curiosity. Similar curiosities about polymers in recent years have led to discoveries of importance in such diverse areas as the manufacture of rubber, the theory of solutions, and the chemistry of life itself.

What are these polymers which are of such economic importance? What in their nature makes them of theoretical interest to the chemist? How are they involved in the life process? In the following pages partial answers are provided to these and other questions about polymers. Complete answers can only be made possible by future years of research.

Polymer molecules are similar to the more familiar simple molecules in that they are held together by the same types of bonding forces. For the sake of simplicity we will consider these forces to be of four types:

1. *Ionic bonds* are quite strong and occur between elements which differ widely in their relative attraction for electrons (electronegativity) and are of little importance in connection with this discussion.

2. *Covalent bonds* are also quite strong, representing an energy of about 50 to 100 kcal per Avogadro's number of bonds. These bonds occur when two elements are similar in their electronegativity and therefore are able to share electrons. The bond energies for some common covalent bonds are listed in Table 1-1.

3. *Hydrogen bonds* are weak in strength, having an energy of about 2 to 5 kcal, and are not completely understood. They generally take the form $A—H \cdots B—C$, where the hydrogen, H, is covalently bound to A, and B is a fairly electronegative atom which is covalently bound to C.

4. *Dipole interactions* are weak forces, less than one kcal, which occur between molecules (or portions of them) where electrical dipoles either exist or can be readily made to exist.

TABLE 1-1.   Approximate Energies of Some Covalent Bonds (kcal/mole)

| | | | |
|---|---|---|---|
| C—H | 98 | C—O | 79 |
| C—C | 80 | O—H | 109 |
| C=C | 145 | O—O | 34 |

A polymer molecule may be defined as a number of repeating chemical units held together by covalent bonds.* A high polymer is one in which the number of repeating units

---

*The above definition is necessary to distinguish polymers from crystals or liquids wherein repeating units are held together by ionic bonds or hydrogen bonds or by even weaker forces such as dipole interactions.

is in excess of about 100. This number is termed the degree of polymerization (D.P.). The molecular weight of a polymer is given by the product of the molecular weight of the repeating unit times D.P. The compound (or compounds) which makes up the repeating unit is termed the monomer. A question which must be answered in order to understand the nature of polymerization reactions is "why does the D.P. achieve values of 100, 1000, or even 10,000 when most chemical reactions are the result of combining only two or three molecules?" The answer to this question can be found in a consideration of the concept of *functional groups*.

All chemical reactions must take place between two functional groups. For example, let us consider one of the most familiar chemical reactions, that of an acid with a base to produce a salt plus water:

$$HA + BOH \rightarrow AB + H_2O \qquad (1\text{-}1)$$

A different sort of example, from organic chemistry, would be the reaction of acetic acid with ethanol to yield ethyl acetate. The underlined carboxyl group makes acetic acid an acid, while the underlined hydroxyl group makes ethanol an alcohol.

$$CH_3\overset{\overset{\displaystyle O}{\|}}{C}\!\!-\!\!\underline{OH} + CH_3CH_2\!\!-\!\!\underline{OH} \rightarrow$$

$$CH_3\overset{\overset{\displaystyle O}{\|}}{C}\!\!-\!\!O\!\!-\!\!CH_2CH_3 + H_2O \qquad (1\text{-}2)$$

In this case the acetic acid may react with the ethanol to give water and ethyl acetate. Both ethanol and acetic acid have only one functional group each, and therefore the reaction between them can be considered to be a one-step process (if we ignore the detailed mechanism of the reaction). This in general is the nature of the reaction between monofunctional compounds.

Suppose instead of ethanol, we react ethylene glycol, a di-hydroxy compound, with acetic acid. We might then expect the reaction to proceed in a similar fashion to reaction 1-2:

$$HOCH_2CH_2OH \ + \ CH_3\overset{\displaystyle O}{\overset{\|}{C}}OH \ \longrightarrow$$

$$CH_3\overset{\displaystyle O}{\overset{\|}{C}}OCH_2CH_2OH \ + \ H_2O \quad (1\text{-}3)$$

This first product still has a hydroxyl group, which may re-act with another acetic acid molecule:

$$CH_3\overset{\displaystyle O}{\overset{\|}{C}}OCH_2CH_2OH \ + \ CH_3\overset{\displaystyle O}{\overset{\|}{C}}OH \ \longrightarrow$$

$$CH_3\overset{\displaystyle O}{\overset{\|}{C}}OCH_2CH_2\overset{\displaystyle O}{\overset{\|}{O C}}CH_3 \ + \ H_2O \quad (1\text{-}4)$$

This is the final product of the reaction, and such is the general result of reactions between mono- and difunctional compounds.

Now let us consider the reaction between two difunctional molecules, such as ethylene glycol and malonic acid. As before, the first reaction might be:

$$HOCH_2CH_2OH \ + \ HO\overset{\displaystyle O}{\overset{\|}{C}}CH_2\overset{\displaystyle O}{\overset{\|}{C}}OH \ \longrightarrow$$

$$HOCH_2CH_2O\overset{\displaystyle O}{\overset{\|}{C}}CH_2\overset{\displaystyle O}{\overset{\|}{C}}OH \ + \ H_2O \quad (1\text{-}5)$$

This compound could then condense with another molecule of acid, with another molecule of glycol, or even with another molecule such as itself. Let us consider the first possibility:

$$\text{HOCH}_2\text{CH}_2\overset{\text{O}}{\overset{\|}{\text{OCCH}_2}}\overset{\text{O}}{\overset{\|}{\text{COH}}} \quad + \quad \text{HO}\overset{\text{O}}{\overset{\|}{\text{CCH}_2}}\overset{\text{O}}{\overset{\|}{\text{COH}}} \quad \rightarrow$$

$$\text{HO}\overset{\text{O}}{\overset{\|}{\text{CCH}_2}}\overset{\text{O}}{\overset{\|}{\text{COCH}_2}}\text{CH}_2\overset{\text{O}}{\overset{\|}{\text{OCCH}_2}}\overset{\text{O}}{\overset{\|}{\text{COH}}} \quad + \quad \text{H}_2\text{O} \quad (1\text{-}6)$$

This compound can now react with a molecule of ethylene glycol at either end to give:

$$\text{HOCH}_2\text{CH}_2\overset{\text{O}}{\overset{\|}{\text{OCCH}_2}}\overset{\text{O}}{\overset{\|}{\text{COCH}_2}}\text{CH}_2\overset{\text{O}}{\overset{\|}{\text{OCCH}_2}}\overset{\text{O}}{\overset{\|}{\text{COH}}} \quad + \quad \text{H}_2\text{O} \quad (1\text{-}7)$$

This compound can now react with either acid or glycol, and so the reaction would continue alternately with acid and glycol. We can write the over-all reaction, then, in the quite general fashion:

$$n \ \text{HOCH}_2\text{CH}_2\text{OH} \quad + \quad n \ \text{HO}\overset{\text{O}}{\overset{\|}{\text{CCH}_2}}\overset{\text{O}}{\overset{\|}{\text{COH}}} \quad \rightarrow$$

$$\text{HO}\overset{}{}\!\!\left(\!\text{CH}_2\text{CH}_2\overset{\text{O}}{\overset{\|}{\text{OCCH}_2}}\overset{\text{O}}{\overset{\|}{\text{CO}}}\!\right)_{\!n}\!\!\text{H} \quad (1\text{-}8)$$

where the product is polymer of D.P. $= n$.

This is the general result of reactions between two difunctional molecules—a linear high polymer. It is easy to visualize that the inclusion of a few trifunctional molecules in the reaction between difunctional molecules would lead to the formation of branched-chain molecules, which could then link together to form cross-linked polymer chains. This is shown schematically in Figure 1-1. The structure of the polymer chain has a very strong influence on the physical properties of the polymer; this will be discussed in detail in Chapter 4.

*Monofunctional molecules*

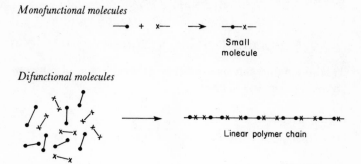

Small molecule

*Difunctional molecules*

Linear polymer chain

*Difunctional molecules plus some trifunctional molecules*

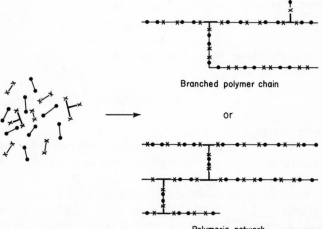

Branched polymer chain

or

Polymeric network

Figure 1-1. Schematic representation of polymer growth.

6

Returning to a consideration of the reaction of product 1-7, it is quite proper to ask "why wouldn't such a compound react with itself to form a cyclic compound such as 1-9?" Such a molecule would be incapable of further ad-

$$
\begin{array}{ccc}
\overset{O}{\overset{\|}{C}}CH_2\overset{O}{\overset{\|}{C}}OCH_2CH_2OH & \overset{O}{\overset{\|}{C}}CH_2\overset{O}{\overset{\|}{C}}OCH_2CH_2 & \\
| & \diagup \qquad \diagdown & \\
O & \longrightarrow \quad O \qquad\qquad O \quad + \;\; H_2O \quad (1\text{-}9) \\
| & | \qquad\qquad\qquad | & \\
CH_2CH_2OC CH_2\overset{}{C}OH & CH_2CH_2OCCH_2C & \\
\quad \overset{\|}{O} \; \overset{\|}{O} & \quad\;\; \overset{\|}{O} \;\; \overset{\|}{O} &
\end{array}
$$

ditions and is obviously not a high polymer. The answer to this is that such reactions are possible but must be viewed as competitive with chain growth. In this competition the "winning" reaction will be the one which happens more often, that is, the one with the greater probability. At the beginning of the reaction, the number of chain ends present is far smaller than the number of glycol or acid molecules present, and therefore it is more probable that the chain end will collide and react with an acid or glycol molecule than with another chain end. When the reaction has proceeded for some time and not many of the original single molecules are left, the chain ends will become quite numerous. It can be shown that the reaction of a chain end with the other end of its own chain is far less probable than with a different chain's end simply because the distance of separation between ends of a given chain is so great. These considerations may be generalized by saying that, except under peculiar circumstances of relative concentrations, chain formation is overwhelmingly favored over ring formation.

Now let us consider the length to which a chain may grow. To do so we will define the following items:

$p$ = the extent of reaction
$N_0$ = the number of molecules initially present
$N_t$ = the number of molecules present at time $t$
$f$ = the functionality of the reacting molecules

We may extend the definition of $p$ by regarding it as the ratio of the number of functional groups used to the number of functional groups originally present. Since each bond formed yields one less molecule, the total number of bonds formed at any time is given by the quantity $(N_0 - N_t)$. Since each bond that is formed consumes two functional groups, the number of functional groups used is $2(N_0 - N_t)$. Therefore:

$$p = 2(N_0 - N_t)/fN_0 \qquad (1\text{-}10)$$

if we realize that the degree of polymerization is given by

$$\text{D.P.} = N_0/N_t \qquad (1\text{-}11)$$

we can then rearrange 1.10 to give

$$\text{D.P.} = 1/(1 - fp/2) \qquad (1\text{-}12)$$

This equation is most fundamental to an understanding of the polymerization process. For example, if we are discussing monofunctional compounds, $f = 1$, and when the reaction is complete (that is, when $p = 1$) then the D.P. will be 2; that is, only two molecules will join as the final product. This we saw in reaction 1-2. If we consider difunctional molecules where $f = 2$, then we can see that the D.P. approaches infinity as $p$ approaches unity. This is a mathematical statement of the fact that, *if* the reaction could proceed to completion, then all the original molecules would be present in a single, virtually infinitely long molecule.* That this is not achieved in fact can be explained by the presence of impurities in any reaction mixture. In the usual organic

*This indeed was a theme in the famous motion picture "The Man in the White Suit."

reaction, a chemist is quite satisfied with a yield of 95%. In a polymerization reaction such as we have discussed proceeding to a 95% yield, $p$ would be 0.95 and the D.P. would therefore be only 20. In order to obtain the not unusual D.P. of 1000, it is necessary to achieve a purity of the reacting components of 99.9%, greater than that of a well-known soap. This extraordinary purity requirement is perhaps the most significant factor in the somewhat delayed development of polymer science as a well-understood branch of chemistry.

One additional consideration of the degree of polymerization must now be treated. This concerns the fact that the growth of chains must be a random process; that is, some chains will grow faster than others. The arithmetical average of all the chain lengths in a given reaction must obey equation 1-12, but there will be a distribution of these lengths which will depend on the exact, statistical laws which govern the competitive process. A possible distribution curve is shown in Figure 1-2. Any collection of data should be

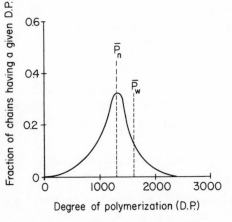

Figure 1-2. Distribution of molecular weights.

characterized by at least two numbers—for example, the average value of the data and the width of the distribution curve. Data for the distribution curve for a polymer are frequently characterized by the ordinary, numerically averaged D.P. ($\overline{P}_n$) and another type of average called the weight average degree of polymerization ($\overline{P}_w$). The reason for using the latter is that certain types of molecular weight measurements, such as light scattering, give a weight average. The spread of molecular weights for a given polymer sample is frequently characterized by the ratio $\overline{P}_w/\overline{P}_n$, a value approaching unity indicating a very narrow spread and a large value indicating a wide distribution.

In the succeeding chapters numerous examples of known polymerization reactions will be given. These reactions are "known" because polymerization is thermodynamically possible and kinetically probable; that is, the reactions occur at a reasonable rate of speed with a change in the Gibbs free energy ($\Delta G$) which is negative. The detailed kinetics of polymerization reactions are too complex to be considered here, but a brief examination of the thermodynamics will prove fruitful.

Consider a propagating polymer chain ($M_n$) of degree of polymerization $n$. Upon addition of a monomer unit, M, the chain will be $(n + 1)$ units long.

$$M_n + M \rightleftharpoons M_{n+1} \qquad (1\text{-}13)$$

On a microscopic scale all chemical reactions are reversible, which is why the above reaction is written as reversible. Ultimately the reaction will come to equilibrium, at which time

$$K_{eq} = [M_{n+1}]/[M_n][M] \qquad (1\text{-}14)$$

If $n$ is sufficiently large, the number of chains having $n$ units will be approximately equal to the number having $(n + 1)$ units.

$$[M_n] \approx [M_{n+1}] \qquad (1\text{-}15)$$

Therefore the equilibrium constant becomes simply the reciprocal of the concentration of monomer present at equilibrium. This is in turn related to the standard change in the Gibbs free energy:

$$K_{eq} = 1/[M]_{eq} \qquad \Delta G° = RT \ln [M]_{eq} \qquad (1\text{-}16)$$

Alternatively, we may consider that the reaction will be at equilibrium when $\Delta G$ is zero. In this case we can see that a critical temperature $(T_c)$ exists at which equilibrium occurs if:

$$\Delta G = \Delta H - T_c \Delta S = 0$$

$$T_c = \Delta H / \Delta S \qquad (1\text{-}17)$$

The temperature $T_c$ has been called a "ceiling" temperature for those polymerizations which have negative enthalpy $(\Delta H)$ and entropy $(\Delta S)$ changes associated with them. The ceiling temperature is defined as that temperature above which monomer cannot be converted into long chain polymer. Conversely, a "floor" temperature exists below which polymerization is not possible if both $\Delta H$ and $\Delta S$ are positive. Striking examples of "ceiling" and "floor" temperatures are seen in the polymerizations of $\alpha$-methylstyrene and sulfur, respectively. These are discussed in subsequent chapters.

# ORGANIC
# POLYMERIZATION
# REACTIONS

A CHEMICAL REACTION between two molecules may be defined as a process in which one or more chemical bonds are formed or broken. The synthetic chemist, be he organic or inorganic, has as his field of study the nature of chemical reactions. Since the number of ways of arranging the more than 100 elements of the Periodic Table—or even just carbon and hydrogen—is virtually infinite, the synthetic chemist's imagination is almost the only boundary placed on his work.

Polymerization reactions differ from ordinary reactions only in that the reacting molecules must have two or more functional groups. Therefore the number of polymerization reactions which are possible is also enormous. It is fortunate for our purposes, however, that only a relatively small number of polymerization reactions have achieved scientific or technological importance. In this chapter we will consider some of the reactions which lead to the formation of frequently encountered polymers, as well as some polymerization reactions which are of interest because of their fundamental importance or potential usefulness.

## Organic Condensation Polymers

In considering the functionality of reacting molecules the example of a reaction between a glycol and a dibasic acid was used. This reaction, which is an esterification, leads to the formation of a *polyester*, and is typical of a process known as polycondensation. In the process a small molecule (water) is formed, and this is sometimes taken as the mark of a condensation process. But more important as an identifying feature for a condensation reaction is the nature of the reactants themselves: there is essentially no difference between the monomer and the polymer insofar as the condensation reaction is concerned. Monomer may react with monomer to form *dimer*, dimer may react with dimer to form *tetramer*. It is also possible for monomer to react with polymer of any chain length and for polymer of any chain length to react with another polymer of any chain length. In all of these reactions, the chemical process is the same, the nature of it being altered very slightly only for the lowest molecular weight reactants. Many of the most important polymers in use are formed by condensation reactions and will now be considered.

*Polyesters.* An esterification reaction must usually be considered as an equilibrium process which proceeds well when it is catalyzed by an acid or base. The example used in Chapter 1 can be generalized as:

$$n\,\overset{O}{\underset{\|}{\text{HOC}}}\overset{O}{\underset{\|}{\text{RCOH}}} \;+\; n\,\text{HOR'OH} \;\underset{\text{catalyst}}{\rightleftharpoons}$$

$$\text{H}\!\left(\!\overset{O}{\underset{\|}{\text{OC}}}\text{R}\overset{O}{\underset{\|}{\text{COR'}}}\!\right)_{\!n}\!\text{OH} \;+\; (n-1)\,\text{H}_2\text{O} \qquad (2\text{-}1)$$

In order to shift the equilibrium to the right and increase the formation of polymer, the water which is formed must be removed continually; this is usually accomplished by distillation.

Polyesters find applications as covering materials in quite diverse ways—as paints, as fabrics, and as flexible films. The alkyd paints are based on polyesters such as that formed between glycerol and phthalic acid. In practice, the anhydride of the acid is used (eq. 2-2), and, since glycerol is

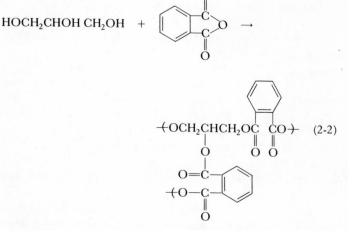

$$\text{HOCH}_2\text{CHOH CH}_2\text{OH} \quad + \qquad \rightarrow \qquad\qquad (2\text{-}2)$$

trifunctional, some difunctional ethylene glycol is added to control the amount of cross-linking in the polymer. It is also possible to control the cross-linking through the use of a monofunctional acid.

The fabric Dacron and the film Mylar have the same chemical composition, their readily apparent physical differences being due to mechanical processing. They are produced from the polyester of ethylene glycol and terephthalic acid. In the actual process (eq. 2-3), the terephthalic acid is used as its methyl ester, which is more readily purified. This type of reaction is termed an ester interchange. Note

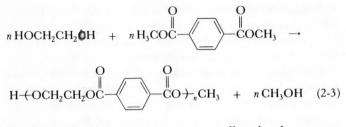

$$n \, HOCH_2CH_2OH \; + \; n \, H_3COC - \underset{O}{\overset{O}{\parallel}} - \underset{O}{\overset{O}{\parallel}} - COCH_3 \; \rightarrow$$

$$H + OCH_2CH_2OC - \underset{O}{\overset{O}{\parallel}} - CO +_n CH_3 \; + \; n \, CH_3OH \quad (2\text{-}3)$$

that it is still necessary to remove a small molecule to upset the equilibrium in the desired direction. In this case it is methanol, whereas in the straightforward esterification it is water that must be removed.

*Polyamides.* Organic amines may be considered as nitrogen analogs of alcohols, where the —OH functional group is replaced by an —$NH_2$ group. In a similar way the nitrogen analog of an ester is an amide, formed by the reaction of an acid with an amine. An amide may also be formed by reaction between an amine and an acid anhydride or acid chloride. Still a third method involves the heating of a salt of the amine and acid. In this manner the most familiar synthetic polyamide, nylon, is produced from the salt of adipic acid and hexamethylenediamine (eq. 2-4). The salt formed

$$n \, H_2N + CH_2 \rightarrow_6 NH_2 \; + \; n \, HOC + CH_2 \rightarrow_4 COH \; \rightarrow \; n \, [\text{SALT}]$$

$$n \, [\text{SALT}] \; \underset{\Delta}{\rightleftharpoons} \; H + HN(CH_2)_6 NHC(CH_2)_4 C +_n OH \; + \; n \, H_2O$$
$$(2\text{-}4)$$

by mixing approximately equimolar quantities of the two compounds may be purified by recrystallization. This guarantees an exactly equimolar ratio of the two ingredients. Were this salt heated it would then produce an extremely high molecular weight product according to equation 1-12.

Control of the molecular weight is achieved by the deliberate addition of an excess of monofunctional amine or acid. As in esterification, amide formation is an equilibrium process, and the water produced must be removed.

The nylon produced by reaction 2-4 is frequently termed nylon 66, since the amine and the acid both contain six carbon atoms. Other nylons have been prepared with varying numbers of carbon atoms. Of particular interest is a nylon prepared from the cyclic lactam of aminocaproic acid (eq. 2-5). This polymer, known as nylon 6, has properties

$$n \; \underset{\substack{H_2 \\ H_2 \quad H_2}}{\overset{\substack{H_2 \\ H_2 \quad O}}{\underset{}{\bigcirc}}} \mspace \xrightarrow[\Delta]{H_2O} \; H[HN(CH_2)_5\overset{O}{\overset{\|}{C}}]_n OH \qquad (2\text{-}5)$$

similar to nylon 66 and is competitive with it. The ring-opening reaction may be catalyzed by a trace of water.

When a difunctional amine and a difunctional acid chloride are mixed in a common solvent, a polyamide and hydrochloric acid are produced:

$$n \, H_2NRNH_2 \;+\; n \, Cl\overset{O}{\overset{\|}{C}}R'\overset{O}{\overset{\|}{C}}Cl \;\longrightarrow$$

$$\mspace{80mu} +\!\!\Big(HNRNH\overset{O}{\overset{\|}{C}}R'\overset{O}{\overset{\|}{C}}\Big)\!\!\Big{)}_n \;+\; n \, HCl \qquad (2\text{-}6)$$

The polymer formed in this manner is usually of a low molecular weight.

It is also possible to dissolve the same reactants separately in mutually immiscible liquids. When these two solutions are brought together, polymer forms at the interface. This polymer is of a quite high molecular weight. If one liquid is layered onto the other, a film is formed which may be picked up and a continuous strand drawn off from the interface. The "nylon rope trick," performed in this way, makes an interesting experiment or demonstration, for which complete directions are provided in the *Journal of Chemical Education* **36,** 182 (1959).

Chemists have been making polyamides for commercial purposes for some thirty years. Natural polyamides, called proteins, have been in production since the first organism reproduced itself. Proteins are discussed in detail in Chapter 6.

*Polyurethanes.* The functional group $-N=C=O$ is called the isocyanate group and is capable of some extremely versatile reactions. Most important for our consideration is its ability to react with many substances bearing active hydrogens, such as water, alcohols, and amines.

$$RN=C=O \ + \ H_2O \ \rightarrow \ RNH\overset{\overset{\displaystyle O}{\|}}{C}OH \qquad (2\text{-}7)$$

The product of reaction 2-7 is a urethane which can be decomposed to give an amine and carbon dioxide gas.

$$RNH\overset{\overset{\displaystyle O}{\|}}{C}OH \ \rightarrow \ RNH_2 \ + \ CO_2 \qquad (2\text{-}8)$$

The amine can then react with another isocyanate group to produce a urea.

$$RNH_2 \ + \ RN=C=O \ \rightarrow \ RNH\overset{\overset{\displaystyle O}{\|}}{C}NHR \qquad (2\text{-}9)$$

Polymerization can be carried out by reacting, for example, tetramethylene glycol and hexamethylene diisocyanate.

$$n\,HO(CH_2)_4OH \quad + \quad n\,O{=}C{=}N(CH_2)_6N{=}C{=}O \quad \rightarrow$$

$$\underset{}{\left[ O(CH_2)_4O\overset{\overset{O}{\|}}{C}NH(CH_2)_6NH\overset{\overset{O}{\|}}{C} \right]_n} \quad (2\text{-}10)$$

It is also possible to produce what are known as urethane foams, either flexible or rigid, by using polyesters having hydroxyl end groups. The latter are prepared by reacting a dibasic acid with an excess of glycol. All the chain ends will then be alcoholic in nature and the reaction sequence might be as shown in equation 2-11 (PE stands for polyester chain).

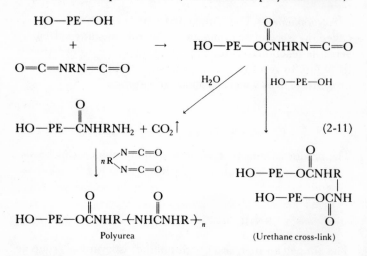

(2-11)

Polyurea                     (Urethane cross-link)

All of these reactions would lead to a cross-linked mass of polymer chains, some polyester, some polyurea, having urethane linkages. The evolution of carbon dioxide can be controlled by the amount of water added to the reaction mixture. It is thereby possible to attain the degree of foaming and cross-linking which is desired.

As described above, the urethane foams are obviously not simple polymers. In the next section we will discuss epoxy resins which are also not simple polymers. Later in the chapter we will discuss *copolymers* in some detail. Both the urethane foams and epoxy resins can be considered as special types of copolymers, but their chemistry more conveniently places them under the heading of condensation polymers.

**Epoxy Resins.** The epoxy group $\overset{O}{\overset{\diagup\diagdown}{C-C}}$ is similar to the isocyanate group discussed above in that it is capable of undergoing a number of diverse reactions, for example, with amines, alcohols, and acids.

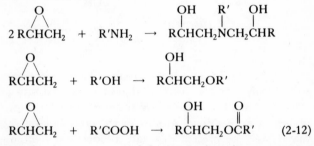

$$2\ R\overset{O}{\overset{\diagup\diagdown}{C}}HCH_2\ +\ R'NH_2\ \rightarrow\ R\overset{OH}{\underset{|}{C}}HCH_2\overset{R'}{\underset{|}{N}}CH_2\overset{OH}{\underset{|}{C}}HR$$

$$R\overset{O}{\overset{\diagup\diagdown}{C}}HCH_2\ +\ R'OH\ \rightarrow\ R\overset{OH}{\underset{|}{C}}HCH_2OR'$$

$$R\overset{O}{\overset{\diagup\diagdown}{C}}HCH_2\ +\ R'COOH\ \rightarrow\ R\overset{OH}{\underset{|}{C}}HCH_2O\overset{O}{\overset{\|}{C}}R' \qquad (2\text{-}12)$$

Use is made of one or more of these reactions in most epoxy resins. Perhaps the most common epoxy is that formed by the reaction of an excess amount of epichlorohydrin (itself an epoxy compound) with a compound commonly known as bisphenol A (which is obviously easier to remember than

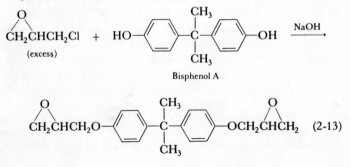

$$CH_2\overset{O}{\overset{\diagup\diagdown}{C}}HCH_2Cl\ +\ HO-\!\!\!\langle\ \rangle\!\!\!-\overset{CH_3}{\underset{CH_3}{\overset{|}{\underset{|}{C}}}}-\!\!\!\langle\ \rangle\!\!\!-OH\ \xrightarrow{NaOH}$$

(excess)

Bisphenol A

$$CH_2\overset{O}{\overset{\diagup\diagdown}{C}}HCH_2O-\!\!\!\langle\ \rangle\!\!\!-\overset{CH_3}{\underset{CH_3}{\overset{|}{\underset{|}{C}}}}-\!\!\!\langle\ \rangle\!\!\!-OCH_2\overset{O}{\overset{\diagup\diagdown}{C}}HCH_2 \qquad (2\text{-}13)$$

its true name: 4,4'-isopropylidenediphenol). This substance is the basic "monomer" of epoxy resins. In the aqueous caustic solution in which it is made, it may polymerize to some extent, depending on how much epichlorohydrin was used in excess. For this type of polymer (2-14) a D.P. of as

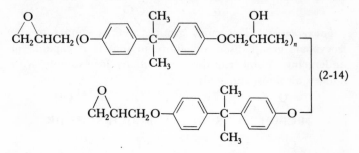

$$(2\text{-}14)$$

low as 10 results in a solid mass. The lower molecular weight polymers are "cured," that is, converted into a solid resinous mass, by cross-linking reactions such as those listed above. The functional groups in the cross-linking reagents may simply be present in small trifunctional molecules, or they may be incorporated in other polymer chains as in urethanes. In any event, the resulting polymers, depending as they do on ether linkages, are relatively inert chemically and find wide application as coatings.

*Formaldehyde Polymers.* The simple compound formaldehyde, $H_2C{=}O$, is capable of entering into a large number of reactions. Formaldehyde has long been known to exist in concentrated aqueous solutions as a short chain polymer called paraldehyde, but only within the past decade was it possible to produce a formaldehyde which was pure enough to yield a high molecular weight polymer, known as Delrin.

$$n\,CH_2{=}O \;+\; H_2O \;\rightarrow\; HO(CH_2O)_n H \qquad (2\text{-}15)$$

Formaldehyde also condenses with phenol to yield a three-dimensional polymer known as Bakelite. This reaction (2-16) is extremely complex and is still not fully understood,

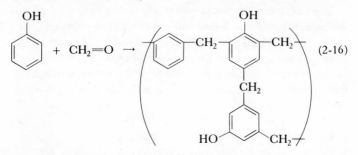

nor is the reaction between formaldehyde and urea (eq. 2-17) or melamine. The polymers formed by the latter are

$$
\begin{array}{c}
\underset{\text{NH}_2}{\overset{\text{NH}_2}{\diagdown}}\text{C}=\text{O} \ + \ \text{CH}_2=\text{O} \ \rightarrow
\end{array}
$$

$$
\begin{array}{c}
\overset{\displaystyle\text{O}}{\overset{\displaystyle\|}{\text{HNCH}_2\text{NHCNH}\text{+}}}\\
|\\
\text{C}=\text{O}\\
|\\
\text{HNCH}_2\text{NCH}_2\text{+} \qquad (2\text{-}17)\\
|\\
\text{C}=\text{O}\\
|\\
\text{HNCH}_2\text{+}
\end{array}
$$

now a household name due to their presence in lightweight dinnerware.

**Polysulfides.** It is well known that elemental sulfur can exist as a polymeric chain, so that it should not be too surprising to find it incorporated into an organic polymer. A whole class of rubbers, known as Thiokol rubbers, has been produced by the reaction between organic dihalides and sodium polysulfide.

$$
\text{Cl(CH}_2)_4\text{Cl} \ + \ \text{Na}_2\text{S}_x \ \rightarrow \ \text{--(CH}_2\text{CH}_2\text{CH}_2\text{CH}_2\text{S}_x\text{)--} \qquad (2\text{-}18)
$$

$$
x \ = \ 2, 3, 4, \ldots
$$

These rubbers have recently become of extreme importance as the major component of the matrix of solid fuel rockets.

The polymers discussed so far do not in any way represent a catalog of the important condensation polymers, but only a listing of some which are of interest. It is worthwhile to emphasize again that the number of polymers which *could* be synthesized is limitless. Many problems of a synthetic nature remain to be solved; this is a fertile area for further research.

### Organic Addition Polymers

In all of the preceding examples the reactions involved a "condensing" together of two molecules, either monomer or polymer. There is no distinction between the functional group on the monomer and the functional group on the polymer in a condensation polymerization. However, there are polymerizations in which such distinctions can arise. These are termed *addition* polymerizations and are best typified by the reactions of the carbon–carbon double bond.

To understand polymerization of molecules containing a carbon–carbon double bond (commonly called *vinyl* polymerization) it is first necessary to explore the nature of the bonding of one carbon atom to another. In Table 1-1 (page 2) it can be seen that a carbon–carbon single bond is held together by 80 kcal/mole. Note that the strength of the double bond is not twice that of the single bond, but only 145 kcal/mole. The significance of this is that the second pair of electrons connecting the two carbon atoms is quite different from the first pair. When two carbon atoms come together to form only a single bond, their electrons are arrayed spatially as in a regular tetrahedron. A combination of two of these atomic orbitals leads to a molecular orbital, called a $\sigma$ (sigma) orbital. When two atoms form a double bond, their electrons may be represented as in Figure 2-1. Note that in

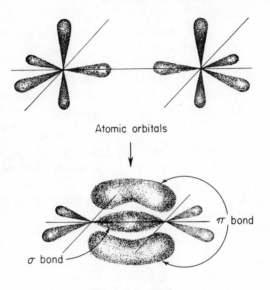

Atomic orbitals

Molecular orbitals

Figure 2-1. Atomic and molecular orbitals.

a given atom three orbitals are coplanar, while the fourth is perpendicular to the plane of the other three. When bond formation occurs, one of the three planar orbitals of each atom combines to form a $\sigma$ orbital, while the perpendicular orbitals combine to form a $\pi$ (pi) orbital.

The electron pair in the $\pi$ orbital is not as strongly held as in the $\sigma$ orbital; hence the double bond energy is less than twice the single bond energy. This fact also means that this extra pair of electrons is quite reactive. Since two carbon atoms are involved, the vinyl functional group (i.e., the carbon–carbon double bond) is difunctional. Insofar as polymerization is concerned, we can consider the three most important reactions of the vinyl group (eqs. 2-19) to be at-

(a)    $R \cdot \ + \ \overset{\diagdown}{\underset{\diagup}{C}} :: \overset{\diagup}{\underset{\diagdown}{C}} \ \rightarrow \ R : \overset{\diagdown}{\underset{\diagup}{C}} : \overset{\diagup}{\underset{\diagdown}{C}} \cdot$

(b)    $R :^- \ + \ \overset{\diagdown}{\underset{\diagup}{C}} :: \overset{\diagup}{\underset{\diagdown}{C}} \ \rightarrow \ R : \overset{\diagdown}{\underset{\diagup}{C}} : \overset{\diagup}{\underset{\diagdown}{C}} :^-$    (2-19)

(c)    $R^+ \ + \ \overset{\diagdown}{\underset{\diagup}{C}} :: \overset{\diagup}{\underset{\diagdown}{C}} \ \rightarrow \ R : \overset{\diagdown}{\underset{\diagup}{C}} : \overset{\diagup}{\underset{\diagdown}{C}}^+$

tack by one of three species: (a) a free radical, (b) a nega-
tively charged Lewis base, or (c) a positively charged Lewis
acid.

These three species can all be produced from the cleavage
of a chemical bond composed of a single pair of electrons. If
the bond between two atoms, A and B, is broken and one
electron is retained by each atom, it is a *homolytic* cleavage
and two free radicals are formed. If one atom, say B, re-
tains both electrons in a *heterolytic* cleavage, then two ions
are formed, $B^-$ being a Lewis base and $A^+$ a Lewis acid.

*Homolytic cleavage:*    $A : B \ \rightarrow \ A \cdot \ + \ B \cdot$

*Heterolytic cleavage:*    $A : B \ \rightarrow \ A^+ \ + \ B^-$    (2-20)

Vinyl polymerization is conveniently divided into free radical and ionic polymerization processes. The latter will be
discussed in some detail in Chapter 5.

**Free Radical Vinyl Polymerization.**   In Table 2-1 are listed
some of the more common vinyl type monomers and their
structures. The polymers derived from free radical polymerization of many of these monomers are familiar to all.
Polyethylene and polystyrene are the two highest in terms of
total production. Polymethylmethacrylate is most familiar
as Plexiglass or Lucite. Butadiene is a source of synthetic
rubber. Vinyl chloride polymers are found in such diverse
applications as piping and raincoats. Polytetrafluoroethyl-
ene (Teflon) is probably the most inert polymer known

and has many applications where this property is necessary, such as in valves for corrosive fluids.

TABLE 2-1.    Structures of Some Vinyl Monomers

| | |
|---|---|
| Ethylene | $H_2C{=}CH_2$ |
| Propylene | $H_2C{=}CHCH_3$ |
| Styrene | $H_2C{=}CH-$ ⬡ |
| Methyl methacrylate | $\begin{matrix} H_3C & O \\ \| & \| \\ H_2C{=}C-COCH_3 \end{matrix}$ |
| Butadiene | $H_2C{=}CHCH{=}CH_2$ |
| Isoprene | $\begin{matrix} CH_3 \\ \| \\ H_2C{=}CCH{=}CH_2 \end{matrix}$ |
| Vinyl chloride | $H_2C{=}CHCl$ |
| Vinyl acetate | $\begin{matrix} O \\ \| \\ H_2C{=}CHOCCH_3 \end{matrix}$ |
| Acrylonitrile | $H_2C{=}CHC{\equiv}N$ |
| Tetrafluoroethylene | $F_2C{=}CF_2$ |

One sequence of reactions (eqs. 2-21) is common to all free radical vinyl polymerizations. It begins with the production of a free radical which adds to the monomer, initiating a chain. This is followed by many subsequent additions of monomer molecules to the chain, thus propagating the chain. Finally, two growing chains react, mutually destroying their free radicals in a termination step.

(*a*) *Initiation*

$$R{-}R \;\rightarrow\; 2R\cdot$$

$$R\cdot \;+\; CH_2{=}CHX \;\rightarrow\; RCH_2\overset{\displaystyle H}{\underset{\displaystyle X}{C}}\cdot$$

(b) *Propagation*

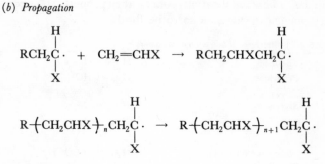

(c) *Termination*

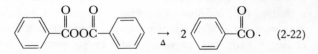

$$R(CH_2CHX)_{n+1}(CHXCH_2)_{m+1}R \quad (2\text{-}21)$$

**Initiation of Polymerization.** The most common source of free radicals for polymerization initiation is the peroxide bond. Compounds such as benzoyl peroxide undergo a homolytic cleavage when heated (eq. 2-22) to give free radi-

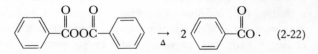

$$(2\text{-}22)$$

cals, and these radicals react very rapidly with monomer to initiate the chain.

However, the initiator fragments may undergo other reactions which will interfere with the initiation. For example, the benzoate radicals might lose $CO_2$ and combine to give biphenyl (eq. 2-23), or they might react with and terminate a growing chain (eq. 2-24). The effects of reactions such as these are grouped under the general term of efficiency of the

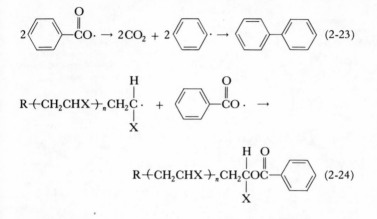

$$2 \bigotimes\text{--}\overset{\overset{O}{\|}}{C}O\cdot \rightarrow 2CO_2 + 2 \bigotimes \cdot \rightarrow \bigotimes\text{--}\bigotimes \qquad (2\text{-}23)$$

$$R\text{--}(CH_2CHX)_n CH_2\overset{\overset{H}{|}}{\underset{X}{C}}\cdot \; + \; \bigotimes\text{--}\overset{\overset{O}{\|}}{C}O\cdot \; \rightarrow$$

$$R\text{--}(CH_2CHX)_n CH_2\overset{\overset{H}{|}}{\underset{X}{C}}\overset{\overset{O}{\|}}{O C}\text{--}\bigotimes \qquad (2\text{-}24)$$

initiator, i.e., that fraction of the initiator which actually initiates polymerization.

*Propagation of Polymerization.* In the course of the propagation reaction hundreds or even thousands of monomer molecules are added to and incorporated in the polymer chain. These molecules, in principle, may be added in one of two ways: "head to tail" or "head to head." Extensive analysis of polymers made by free radical polymerization

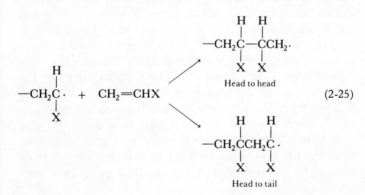

$$-CH_2\overset{\overset{H}{|}}{\underset{X}{C}}\cdot \; + \; CH_2\text{=}CHX$$

Head to head

$$-CH_2\overset{\overset{H}{|}}{\underset{X}{C}}\text{--}\overset{\overset{H}{|}}{\underset{X}{C}}CH_2\cdot$$

Head to tail

$$-CH_2\overset{\overset{H}{|}}{\underset{X}{C}}CH_2\overset{\overset{H}{|}}{\underset{X}{C}}\cdot \qquad (2\text{-}25)$$

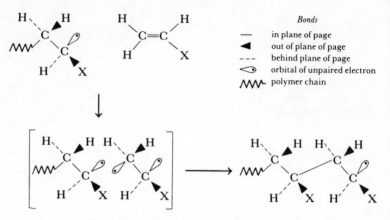

Figure 2-2. Addition of a vinyl monomer to a free radical.

indicates that "head to tail" addition accounts for all but a few per cent of the propagation reaction steps.

Other evidence has shown that the free radical attacks the monomer along the axis of the carbon–carbon double bond. We may therefore represent the propagation reaction in some detail as shown in Figure 2-2. Note that, because of the tetrahedral nature of the bonding about a carbon atom, there is a three-dimensional spatial character to the propagation reaction. This has recently become of importance and will be discussed at length in Chapter 5.

*Termination of Polymerization.* The ultimate length of the chain depends on the relative rates of addition and termination reactions. Actually, the reaction between two free radicals is much faster than the addition of a monomer to a radical, but because there are so many more monomer molecules than free radicals, propagation takes place far more often than termination and a long chain polymer is produced.

The termination reaction may take place in one of two ways. Reaction 2-21(c) illustrates termination by combination of two free radicals. It is also possible to have termination occur by a disproportionation process where a hydrogen atom is abstracted by one chain from the other. Reaction 2-26 is less common than combination but has been experimentally observed.

$$R\left(CH_2CHX\right)_n CH_2\overset{\overset{\textstyle H}{|}}{\underset{\underset{\textstyle X}{|}}{C}} \cdot \quad + \quad R\left(CH_2CHX\right)_m CH_2\overset{\overset{\textstyle H}{|}}{\underset{\underset{\textstyle X}{|}}{C}} \cdot \quad \rightarrow$$

$$R\left(CH_2CHX\right)_n CH_2\overset{\overset{\textstyle H}{|}}{\underset{\underset{\textstyle X}{|}}{C}}H + R\left(CH_2CHX\right)_m CH{=}CHX \quad (2\text{-}26)$$

Another way in which a particular chain may cease growing is by accepting an atom from another molecule, making that molecule a free radical, and thus starting another chain. The process of chain transfer may take place with monomer, solvent, catalyst, polymer, or any impurity in the system. It is illustrated in equation 2-27 for the general case of chain transfer to an "impurity" RH. The impurity may be added as a means of controlling the molecular weight, since deliberate chain transfer results in a lower molecular weight

$$R(CH_2CHX)_n CH_2\overset{\overset{\textstyle H}{|}}{\underset{\underset{\textstyle X}{|}}{C}} \cdot \; + \; RH \; \rightarrow \; R(CH_2CHX)_n CH_2\overset{\overset{\textstyle H}{|}}{\underset{\underset{\textstyle X}{|}}{C}}H \; + \; \overset{\cdot}{R} \cdot$$

$$R \cdot \; + \; CH_2{=}CHX \; \rightarrow \; RCH_2\overset{\overset{\textstyle H}{|}}{\underset{\underset{\textstyle X}{|}}{C}} \cdot \qquad\qquad (2\text{-}27)$$

polymer. On the other hand, RH may be a necessary component of the reaction mixture such as the monomer or solvent.

Vinyl polymerizations may be carried out in bulk—that is, pure monomer with only the initiator added—or in solution. Most polymers are quite soluble in their monomers, and as a bulk polymerization proceeds the solution becomes viscous. Since the termination reaction depends on large chains diffusing toward each other, a viscous reaction medium impedes termination. The concentration of chain ends then increases as does the rate of the reaction and the final stage of the reaction may be faster than the beginning. This is known as autoacceleration and is accompanied by the evolution of a great deal of heat.

If the polymerization is run in a solvent which is capable of dissolving both monomer and polymer, autoacceleration is avoided and a smoother reaction is possible. However, the phenomenon of chain transfer to solvent may occur and limit the maximum molecular weight.

Polymerizations may also be carried out in a two-phase system. In emulsion polymerization, an oily monomer is emulsified in water by means of a soap. Water-soluble initiators can decompose and then diffuse into the emulsified monomer droplets. In effect this leads to bulk polymerizations in a system where the cooling water is inside the reaction flask. Many synthetic rubbers are produced by emulsion polymerization.

## Copolymerization

Up to this point we have considered only those reactions which yield polymers having a repetitive structure and containing only one basic monomer unit. However, it is easy to conceive of polymeric chain structures which contain two or more monomeric units. Such polymers are called *copolymers*. Some of the more common types of copolymers are illustrated below (the letters A, B, and C represent three different monomer units).

Alternating
  copolymer:   —ABABABABAB—

Random
  copolymer:   —ABBBAABAAAABBABABBAB—

Block
  copolymer:   —AAAAAAAAAAAABBBBBBBBBBBBBBB—

Graft
  copolymer:   —AAAAAAAAAAAAAAAAAAAAAAAAAAAA—
```
                  B                    B
                  B                    B
                  B                    B
                  B                    B
                  |                    |
```

Terpolymer:   —ABBACCBACBABCA—

Such intricate structures have unusual properties associated with them which will be discussed in Chapter 4. The syntheses of these copolymers entail many interesting techniques and examples of chemical ingenuity. In fact, in copolymerization the chemist has a process which enables him almost to "tailor-make" molecules whose properties can be reasonably predicted. The technological consequence of such an ability is enormous.

*Polymerization of Mixed Monomers.* If two vinyl monomers are mixed and a free radical catalyst is introduced, polymerization will be propagated via four possible reactions: a chain ending in monomer A can add either another A or a molecule of monomer B; conversely, a chain ending in monomer B can add either another B or A.

(a)   (Copolymer)—A·  +  A  →  (Copolymer)—AA·

(b)   (Copolymer)—A·  +  B  →  (Copolymer)—AB·

(c)   (Copolymer)—B·  +  B  →  (Copolymer)—BB·

(d)   (Copolymer)—B·  +  A  →  (Copolymer)—BA·  (2-28)

These four reactions can be quantitatively described in terms of two reactivity ratios, $r_1$ and $r_2$, which respectively describe the relative rates of reaction $a$ to reaction $b$ and of reaction $c$ to reaction $d$. If both reactivity ratios equal unity, then all four reactions are equally probable and a completely random copolymer will result, as shown above. If both reactivity ratios are zero or nearly so, then reactions $b$ and $d$ will dominate propagation and the resulting polymer will have a strictly alternating structure. An example of the latter situation is the copolymerization of styrene and maleic anhydride. A maleic anhydride free radical is very slow to add another maleic anhydride molecule, thus making the numerator of one reactivity ratio very small, while a styrene free radical reacts extremely rapidly with maleic anhydride, thus making the denominator of the other reactivity ratio quite large. As a consequence both reactivity ratios are so small as to be nearly zero.

Most monomer pairs fall somewhere between the two extremes of strictly random and strictly alternating, as can be seen by inspection of Table 2-2. These reactivity ratios have been obtained experimentally, but there exists a semi-empirical method which enables one to predict reactivity of a given monomer with many others on the basis of copolymerization with only one monomer. This method involves the calculation of two empirical parameters, $Q$ and $e$, from the observed reactivity ratios and the equations:

$$r_1 = (Q_1/Q_2) \exp [-e_1(e_1 - e_2)]$$
$$r_2 = (Q_2/Q_1 \exp [-e_2(e_2 - e_1)] \qquad (2\text{-}29)$$

where $Q$ is the reactivity of the monomer with respect to adding to any free radical, and $e$ is the polarity of the vinyl group. Theoretically, $Q$ and $e$ are constant for any given monomer. Therefore, when $Q$ and $e$ values are known for other monomers, copolymerization reactivities may be calculated without the necessity for laboratory work. That this

TABLE 2-2.  Reactivity Ratios

| Monomer 1 | Monomer 2 | $r_1$ | $r_2$ |
|---|---|---|---|
| Styrene | Butadiene | 0.78 | 1.39 |
| Styrene | Methyl methacrylate | 0.52 | 0.46 |
| Styrene | Maleic anhydride | 0.02 | 0 |
| Vinyl acetate | Methyl methacrylate | 0.015 | 20. |
| Isoprene | Acrylonitrile | 0.45 | 0.03 |

is greatly to be desired may be appreciated from the fact that 100 vinyl monomers may be combined to give a total of 4950 different copolymerizations.

Polymerizations of mixtures of more than two monomers are more difficult to describe.  The number of reactivity ratios required is $n(n - 1)$, where $n$ is the number of monomers in the mixture.  Only six ratios are required for three monomers, but twelve for four.  Quantitative description of a system by so many independent, experimentally determined parameters is difficult but not impossible.

*Graft Copolymerization.*  The formation of a graft copolymer can be brought about by either of two general methods: (1) initiation of chain growth of monomer B on an existing polymer molecule formed from monomer A or (2) termination of chain growth of polymer B by an existing polymer molecule formed from monomer A.  The locus of the reaction in either case is a reactive site somewhere between the ends of polymer A.

In the first case the reactive site can be either pre-existent or formed by chemical attack or high energy radiation.  When a polyamide is treated with ethylene oxide, the amide nitrogen opens the epoxide ring and a graft copolymerization follows (eq. 2-30).

$$\text{\Large\char`\~\char`\~\char`\~}\text{---RCNH}_2 \ + \ n\,\text{CH}_2\text{CH}_2 \ \rightarrow \ \text{\Large\char`\~\char`\~\char`\~}\text{---RCN---\Large\char`\~\char`\~\char`\~} \qquad (2\text{-}30)$$

If polyisoprene is mixed with a vinyl monomer such as methyl methacrylate and benzoyl peroxide, heating of the mixture will produce a graft copolymer *and* some pure polymethylmethacrylate. The reaction is believed to proceed as shown in 2-31. Unfortunately it is not possible to obtain a pure graft copolymer in this fashion. However, the copolymer will have different solution properties and may be separated from the homopolymer by solvent extraction or selective precipitation of one component from solution.

$R\text{---}R \rightarrow 2R\cdot$

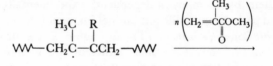

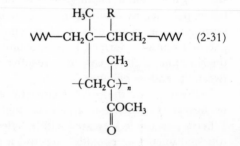

(2-31)

One can prepare pure graft copolymers by incorporating the initiator into the polymer chain. For example, if some *p*-isopropylstyrene is copolymerized in a random fashion with styrene and then the isopropyl group oxidized to a hydroperoxide, chain initiation of another vinyl monomer can be induced by the giant hydroperoxide molecule (eq. 2-32).

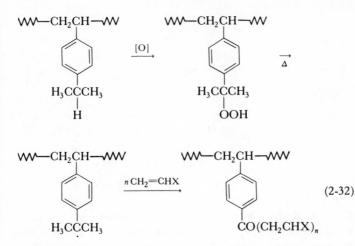

$$(2\text{-}32)$$

Radiation of a polymeric chain may produce ions or free radicals on the chain which can then initiate the growth of a grafted chain. Such a process is attractive for modifying only the surface properties of a film or fiber with respect to such uses as printing on the film or lowering the static electricity on a fiber. For example, polyethylene terephthalate can be irradiated by ultraviolet light in the presence of acrylonitrile and a photosensitizer to yield a graft copolymer. The photosensitizer serves to absorb the energy of the radiation and transfer the energy to the nonabsorbing polymer.

The second general method for producing graft copolymers is somewhat narrower in scope and almost always results in the production of a considerable fraction of homopolymer. For condensation polymerizations we may consider the backbone chain as a giant monofunctional reactant in the condensation reaction as in 2-33. In this case the polymer chain may terminate one or more growing chains, depending on how many functional groups are on the backbone. In free radical polymerization the polymer chain be-

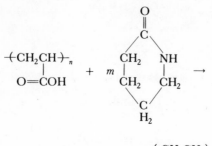

$$\left(CH_2CH\right)_n \quad + \quad m \quad \begin{array}{c} \\ \end{array} \quad \rightarrow$$

$$\begin{array}{c} \left(CH_2CH\right)_n \\ | \\ O=C[NH(CH_2)_5C]_mOH \end{array} \quad (2\text{-}33)$$

haves as a chain transfer reagent. The formation of graft copolymers then depends on the existence of a labile atom, such as a tertiary hydrogen, which can participate in transfer reactions as in 2-34. Halides and mercaptans are also facile chain transfer reagents.

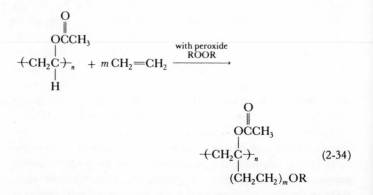

$$\begin{array}{c} O \\ \| \\ OCCH_3 \\ | \\ \left(CH_2C\right)_n \\ | \\ H \end{array} \quad + \quad m\,CH_2{=}CH_2 \quad \xrightarrow[\text{ROOR}]{\text{with peroxide}}$$

$$\begin{array}{c} O \\ \| \\ OCCH_3 \\ | \\ \left(CH_2C\right)_n \\ | \\ (CH_2CH_2)_mOR \end{array} \quad (2\text{-}34)$$

A reaction which is most useful in laminating glass fibers involves a graft copolymerization of a slightly different sort. Maleic acid is incorporated into a polyester which is then re-acted with styrene monomer and a free radical initiator. In the course of the polymerization of the styrene, it will rapidly react with the maleic acid double bond and then, as discussed above, will rapidly add another styrene. The chain propagation therefore results in a network of polyester chains crosslinked by polystyrene chains containing maleic acid. The reaction is illustrated in 2-35 with PE and PS representing polyester and polystyrene chains.

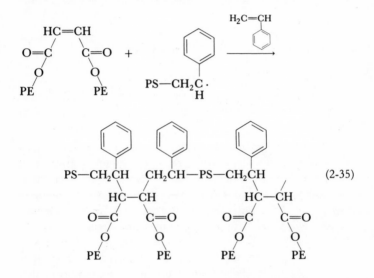

(2-35)

*Block Copolymerization.* In principle it is possible to synthesize block copolymers by one of two methods: link reactive end groups of two different polymer chains or initiate the polymerization of another monomer by the reactive end of a polymer chain. In practice, the latter method is preferable because the concentration of chain ends is so small in a polymer sample that reaction depending on the meeting of two chain ends would be extremely slow.

As in graft copolymerization, a great variety of techniques

exist for producing block copolymers. The various methods may be generalized into four categories: (1) utilize reactive end groups, (2) activate end groups, (3) fragment a chain to produce active end groups, or (4) transport reactive end groups into a different media.

Perhaps the most striking example of the first technique is the initiation of ethylene oxide polymerization by hydroxyl-terminated polypropylene oxide chains (eq. 2-36). These

$$\left(CH_2CHO\right)_n CH_2CHOH \ + \ m \ \overset{O}{\overset{\triangle}{CH_2CH_2}} \ \longrightarrow$$
$$\underset{CH_3}{} \qquad \underset{CH_3}{}$$

$$\left(CH_2CHO\right)_{n+1}\left(CH_2CH_2O\right)_m H \quad (2\text{-}36)$$
$$\underset{CH_3}{}$$

block copolymers, known as Pluronics or Tetronics depending on their detailed structure, have a miscibility with water which is dependent primarily on the fraction of ethylene oxide block which they contain. These block copolymers may in turn be copolymerized by reaction with a diisocyanate to yield a urethane type polymer, in a reaction similar to 2-11.

Anionic polymerization of vinyl monomers offers another excellent example of the first technique. Discussion of this will be deferred to Chapter 5.

The second general technique may be illustrated by the use of carbon tetrabromide as a chain transfer agent in the polymerization of styrene via free radicals (eq. 2-37). The resultant polymer, which may be regarded as a macrohalide molecule, when irradiated with ultraviolet light in the presence of another vinyl monomer (eq. 2-38), will serve to initiate the polymerization of that monomer.

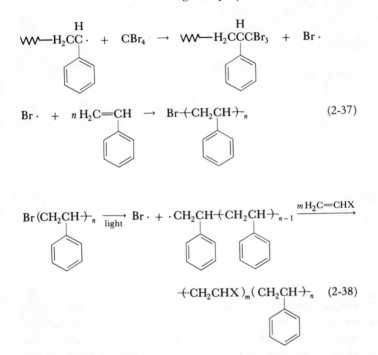

$$(2\text{-}37)$$

$$(2\text{-}38)$$

A variation on the same general technique is the use of a dihydroperoxide. It is possible to initiate the polymerization at a temperature such that many of the polymer chains will have a hydroperoxy end group (eq. 2-39). Raising the temperature on such a polymer chain will cause the peroxy group to cleave and yield two free radicals which can initiate the polymerization of another monomer. One of these will produce a block copolymer, the other will produce homopolymer.

When some monomers, such as methyl methacrylate, are allowed to undergo free radical polymerization in the pres-

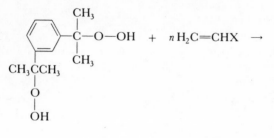

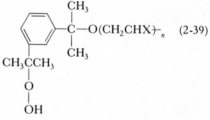

ence of oxygen, a small amount of the oxygen may be incorporated into the polymer making it essentially a giant peroxide. Heating such a polymer will cause it to split homolytically into two macroradicals, each of which can then initiate the polymerization of another monomer; this demonstrates the third general technique for synthesizing block copolymers.

$$R \cdot \ + \ CH_2{=}CHX \ + \ O_2 \ \rightarrow$$

$$\text{\small\wedge\wedge\wedge}{-}CH_2CHXO{-}OCH_2CHX{-}\text{\small\wedge\wedge\wedge} \xrightarrow{\Delta}$$

$$\text{\small\wedge\wedge\wedge}{-}CH_2CHXO \cdot \quad (2\text{-}40)$$

It is not necessary to have what amounts to a "weak link" in the polymer chain in order to cleave it. For example, rubber (polyisoprene) may be cleaved by mechanical shearing forces such as those involved in a milling or calendaring operation, and it has been demonstrated that if another mono-

mer, such as methyl methacrylate, is present, block copolymers will be formed. Chains have also been split homolytically by heat, sonic vibrations, and ultraviolet light.

The fourth general technique involves the transportation
of reactive end groups into another media. When applied to
condensation polymerizations, this is essentially indis-
tinguishable from the first procedure discussed. However,
when vinyl free radical polymerizations are considered, the
extreme reactivity and resultant short lifetime of the free
radical chain ends make this type of technique unique.

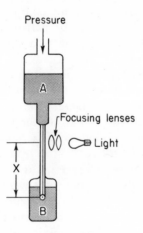

Figure 2-3

One method is illustrated in Figure 2-3. Monomer A in
the upper vessel is allowed to flow through a capillary into
the lower vessel containing a different monomer, B. Polymerization is initiated photochemically at some point along
the capillary. The distance $X$ is varied so that many of the
chains containing monomer A have not yet terminated themselves when they flow into monomer B. Since B will be

greatly in excess of A at this point, mostly block copolymer will result. Some homopolymer of A will have been produced by termination before reaching the lower vessel, but the amount of this can be varied by controlling the distance $X$ and the flow rate of the monomer A solution.

Another method involves the use of a two-phase system. One phase may be considered an "oil" phase and the other an "aqueous" phase. If two monomers are chosen such as styrene which is only oil soluble and acrylic acid which is only water soluble, then it is possible to produce a block copolymer by using an oil soluble free radical initiator. The initiation will all take place in the oil phase, and, if the two phases are intimately mixed, the polymerization which began in the oil phase will conclude in the aqueous phase yielding a block copolymer.

A final example of the technique of transporting radicals into a different medium represents also a proof of an unusual phenomenon. Most vinyl monomers are reasonably good solvents for their polymers, but acrylonitrile is a strong exception. In fact, when acrylonitrile is polymerized in bulk, the polymer precipitates out as the reaction proceeds. Investigation of the unusual kinetics of this reaction led to the postulate that free radical chain ends were being trapped in the "microgel" which formed. One verification for this postulate resides in the fact that if the microgel is dissolved in a solvent for polyacrylonitrile containing another vinyl monomer, a block copolymer will be formed.

*chapter three* ─────────────────────────

# INORGANIC
# POLYMERIZATION
# REACTIONS

THE PREVIOUS chapters dealt with the fundamental principles governing polymerization and their application to what may be considered purely organic molecules. It must be realized that these same principles can be applied to systems which are totally inorganic or a mixture of organic and inorganic. In fact, we can find examples of inorganic condensation polymerizations and addition polymerizations. We can also consider a third type called coordination polymerization.

The fact that these types of polymers are not as familiar as the organic polymers is attributable to two circumstances. In the first place, many inorganic polymerizations lead to highly cross-linked polymers which are physically intractable and therefore of limited technological value. In the second place, the inorganic chemist deals with the entire periodic chart, and his theoretical knowledge of the nature of bonding between the more than 100 elements in the periodic system is far from being fully developed. As a consequence, it is difficult to predict, *a priori*, which inorganic reactions will lead to useful polymers, and which will lead to either no reaction or a useless, brittle mass in the reaction flask.

Certain empirical observations have been made which can serve as guides for consideration of polymers with noncarbon backbones. There is, for example, the phenomenon of *catenation*, the ability of atoms of a particular element to form bonds between themselves. This ability is most predominant for carbon and rapidly diminishes as we consider elements further and further away from carbon in the periodic system. Silicon exhibits this property to some extent, as do nitrogen, sulfur, and the elements beneath them in the periodic chart. For oxygen, the halogens, and the group IIIb elements catenation is limited to the formation of one or two covalent bonds. Therefore, except for a few cases, we must expect that any useful inorganic polymers will contain backbones which are composed of two or more elements, probably arranged in a regular alternating sequence of some sort. It is the task of the inorganic polymer chemist to find those sequences of elements which will yield stable polymeric molecules. Such a task includes the fundamental problem of understanding the nature of bonding more completely and is given an added urgency by the material requirements of the space age, which have already pushed beyond the temperature limits of most organic polymers.

### Inorganic Condensation Polymerizations

In this and the following sections a number of examples will be given to illustrate the enormous variety of reactions which can yield inorganic polymers.

As noted above, silicon exhibits a tendency toward catenation. In the case of the silicon hydrides, for example, the compounds $H(SiH_2)_nH$ are known for values of $n$ up to six. This is hardly a high polymer, but if one synthesizes a siloxane, $\left(\text{R}_2\text{SiO}\right)_n$, formula weights in the millions are possible. This illustrates the point made above that alternating sequences are more likely to yield stable inorganic polymers.

The synthesis of these long chain siloxanes may be accomplished by condensation of silanols, which in turn can be produced from the hydrolysis of halosilanes, as shown in equation 3-1. The degree of polymerization is dependent on

$$
n \underset{\underset{\text{R}}{|}}{\overset{\overset{\text{R}}{|}}{\text{ClSiCl}}} + 2n\,\text{H}_2\text{O} \longrightarrow n \underset{\underset{\text{R}}{|}}{\overset{\overset{\text{R}}{|}}{\text{HOSiOH}}} + 2n\,\text{HCl}
$$

$$\downarrow \qquad\qquad (3\text{-}1)$$

$$
\underset{\underset{\text{R}}{|}}{\overset{\overset{\text{R}}{|}}{\text{HO(SiO)}_n\text{H}}} + (n-1)\,\text{H}_2\text{O}
$$

the extent of reaction, just as described by equation 1-12. If a cross-linked polymer is desired, then silanols of higher functionality can be incorporated into the monomer, or the linear polymer formed from the difunctional silanol can be cross-linked via the substituent R groups.

Phosphorus pentachloride may be partially hydrolyzed to yield dichlorophosphoric acid, which on heating loses HCl to form a low molecular weight polymer (eq. 3-2).

If ammonia (or an amine) is added to diborane, an adduct is obtained which can undergo polymerization upon heating. The first product is the trimeric borazine, which is isoelectronic with benzene and quite stable. Further

$$n\,\mathrm{PCl_5} \;+\; 2n\,\mathrm{H_2O} \;\longrightarrow\; n\,\underset{\underset{\mathrm{Cl}}{|}}{\overset{\overset{\mathrm{O}}{\|}}{\mathrm{HOPCl}}} \;+\; 3n\,\mathrm{HCl}$$

$$\Big\downarrow \Delta \qquad\qquad (3\text{-}2)$$

$$\mathrm{H}\!\!-\!\!\Big(\!\!\underset{\underset{\mathrm{Cl}}{|}}{\overset{\overset{\mathrm{O}}{\|}}{\mathrm{OP}}}\!\!\Big)\!\!\!\!-_{\!n}\mathrm{Cl} \;+\; (n-1)\,\mathrm{HCl}$$

heating produces polymeric material and boron nitride (eq. 3-3). If amines and substituted diboranes are used in

$$2\,\mathrm{NH_3} \;+\; \mathrm{B_2H_6} \;\longrightarrow\; 2\,\mathrm{NH_3BH_3}$$

$$3n\,\mathrm{NH_3BH_3} \;\xrightarrow[\Delta]{-\mathrm{H_2}}\; n \quad\cdots\quad \xrightarrow[\Delta]{-\mathrm{H_2}}\; \text{(HB}\!\!=\!\!\text{N)}_n \;\xrightarrow[\Delta]{-\mathrm{H_2}}\; \mathrm{BN}$$

$$(3\text{-}3)$$

the above reactions, then the substituted borazine (properly called an iminoborane trimer) is too stable to yield a linear polymer. This points up a perplexing problem in the preparation of inorganic polymers, namely, the inability to prepare monomers, or the immense stability of very low polymers such as dimers or trimers.

In aqueous solutions, aggregates of cations or anions can formally be considered to be products of polymerization reactions. The precipitation of metallic hydroxides such as $\mathrm{Fe(OH)_3}$ from alkaline solutions probably proceeds via a complex path that involves the disruption of existing hydrolytic equilibria and the formation of metal–oxygen bonds.

The mechanism of such reactions is still not completely clear.

### Inorganic Addition Polymerizations

Elemental sulfur is known to exist as a cyclic $S_8$ molecule at moderate temperatures. When this is heated, it melts to give a liquid of low viscosity. However, as the temperature of the liquid is increased beyond 160°C, the viscosity also increases—a most unusual phenomenon for liquids. The magnitude of this increase is illustrated in Figure 3-1; it is

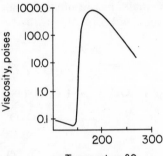

Figure 3-1. Viscosity of molten sulfur.

most intense at about 187°C. From numerous physical measurements and calculations it is possible to explain this behavior in terms of a homolytic cleavage of the $S_8$ ring to yield a diradical which then initiates a free radical polymerization:

$$\begin{array}{c} S-S \\ S \qquad S \\ | \qquad | \\ S \qquad S \\ S-S \end{array} \rightleftharpoons \ \cdot SS_6S \cdot \ \xrightarrow{S_8} \ \cdot SS_{14}S \cdot \quad etc. \qquad (3\text{-}4)$$

The resultant molten polymer is highly viscous owing to chain entanglements. Actually, these reactions are best considered as equilibrium reactions (as discussed in Chapter 1), and the whole process has been quantitatively treated in this fashion. The values of $\Delta H$ and $\Delta S$ for the propagation are $+3.3$ kcal/mole and $+7.35$ cal/degree/mole, respectively. The existence of a predicted floor temperature is obvious in Figure 3-1. Similar treatments have been applied to selenium and copolymers of selenium and sulfur.

Sulfur trioxide can be prepared in a number of modifications. One of these is trimeric and can be polymerized by the addition of a small amount of water, possibly according to a mechanism such as 3-5.

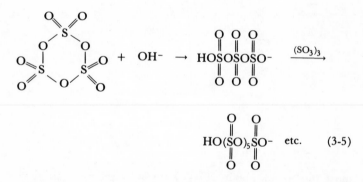

$$\text{HO(SO)}_5\text{SO}^- \quad \text{etc.} \qquad (3\text{-}5)$$

In reaction 3-2, it was shown how controlled hydrolysis of $PCl_5$ led to a monomeric dichlorophosphoric acid, which was capable of undergoing condensation polymerization. If $PCl_5$ is reacted with ammonium chloride, it will yield a mixture of phosphonitrilic halides.

$$\text{PCl}_5 \;+\; \text{NH}_4\text{Cl} \;\rightarrow\; \underset{(\text{I})}{(\text{PNCl}_2)_n} \;+\; \underset{(\text{II})}{(\text{PNCl})_m\text{PCl}_5} \qquad (3\text{-}6)$$

The exact nature of the products depends on the conditions, but compound I is predominantly cyclic trimer and tetramer, while compound II has yet to be fully characterized. If the trimer or tetramer molecules are heated, a rubbery polymer will be produced. This polymerization is catalyzed by a variety of substances such as alcohols, acids, tin, and sodium metal. A plausible reaction scheme has been suggested (eq. 3-7) according to which, primarily on the

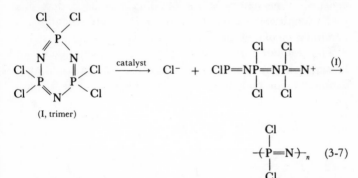

(I, trimer)

$$-(P=N)_n \quad (3\text{-}7)$$

basis of the kinetics of the reaction, a chlorine atom is abstracted from the cyclic "monomer," inducing ring opening. The ionic species thus produced is capable of propagating an addition polymerization.

As seen in previous examples, sulfur readily enters into polymeric chains. Another instance of this is provided by copolymers of sulfur dioxide with vinyl compounds such as propylene. The reaction is apparently a typical free radical addition one, but yields a copolymer in which the two monomers are strictly alternating.

$$n\,CH_3CH=CH_2 \;+\; n\,SO_2 \xrightarrow{\text{benzoyl peroxide}} -(CCS)_n \quad (3\text{-}8)$$

## Coordination Polymers

There exists a type of compound formed by the addition of apparently saturated molecules to each other. These molecular addition or coordination compounds have a peculiar sort of bonding, the nature of which is difficult to describe in purely ionic or covalent terms. Their chemistry was first elucidated by A. Werner at the turn of the century. The nature of the bonding has been described by Pauling's valence bond approach and more recently by a combination of molecular orbital and ligand field theories.

The simplest sort of molecular addition compound is illustrated by aluminum chloride, which is dimeric in the vapor state, or palladium chloride, which exists as a linear polymer.

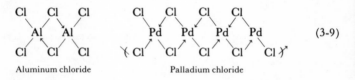

(3-9)

Aluminum chloride            Palladium chloride

More complex coordination compounds involve difunctional compounds, such as ethylenediamine, which are bound to a central metal ion, frequently a transition metal. One such is the tris(ethylenediamine)chromium(III) ion (3-10).

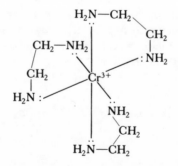

(3-10)

The most common forms for this type of complex compound are octahedral, tetrahedral, or square planar. As soon as polyfunctionality is encountered, the possibility of polymer formation becomes obvious. As an example, the reaction between chromium(III) acetylacetonate and diphenylphosphinic acid leads to the polymer shown in Figure 3-2. This polymer has chromium-centered octahedra

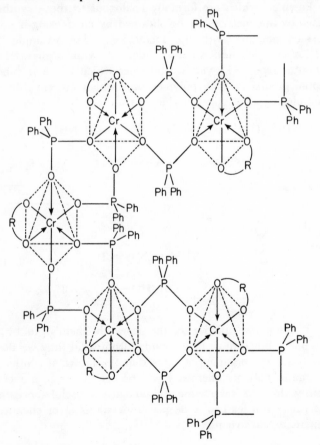

Figure 3-2. Polymer of di-$\mu$-diphenylphosphinatoacetylacetonatochromium(III).

linked together by phosphorus atoms. The geometry of the bonding leads to the spiral structure shown.

Many polymers have been synthesized in the above fashion. However, detailed study of such syntheses is hampered by the fact that the resultant polymers are frequently insoluble or cross-linked, and, as a consequence, are difficult to characterize.

Polymers which are formally analogous to those synthesized by this method can be obtained by condensing a preformed polymer with the metal ion. For example, a bis(salicylaldehyde), when condensed with *o*-phenylenediamine (eq. 3-11), yields a polymer which has four functional groups in each polymer unit which are capable of complexing with copper or zinc ions.

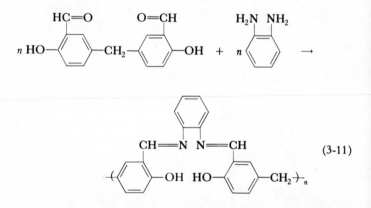

(3-11)

It is not the function of the research chemist to be a prophet. But it must be concluded from what little we now know about inorganic polymers that the future of synthetic inorganic polymer chemistry will be bright, for it is a certainty that the search for technologically useful inorganic polymers will lead to a deeper understanding of chemical reactivity and structure.

*chapter four* ————————————————————

# PHYSICAL BEHAVIOR
# OF POLYMERS

WHEN ONLY low molecular weight substances are being considered, it is possible to divide matter into the three categories of crystalline solid, liquid, and gas. (The glassy state sometimes encountered with low molecular weight compounds may be considered a supercooled liquid.) Polymeric materials sometimes fit one or another of these categories, but deserve special consideration because of the peculiar properties attributed to their very long chain lengths. For convenience we will separately consider the behavior of polymers when dissolved in solvents and when present as pure or only slightly adulterated substances. Solution behavior is of importance because we can learn much about the molecular attributes of polymers from the properties of their solutions. The behavior of the bulk polymer is of importance since it is in this form that most polymers are of technological use.

## Solution Properties—Molecular Weight Measurements

The most fundamental singular aspect of high polymers is the fact that their molecular weights are several orders of magnitude larger than those of more conventional molecules.

This fact makes the determination of molecular weights of polymers of primary importance. It also creates a somewhat difficult experimental task.

Three colligative properties are commonly employed for molecular weight measurements: freezing point depression, $\Delta T$; vapor pressure lowering, $\Delta P$; and osmotic pressure, $\pi$. As the term "colligative" implies, these properties are a function only of the *number* of solute molecules present in a given volume of solution. It is possible to derive from thermodynamic principles expressions relating these properties to the *activity* of the solute. These expressions are quite simple in form for dilute solutions:

$$\Delta T = (RT^2/\Delta H°)a \qquad (4\text{-}1)$$

where $T$ is normal boiling (or freezing) point of solvent, $R$ is the gas constant, $\Delta H°$ is standard heat of vaporization (or fusion) of solvent, and $a$ is solute activity;

$$\Delta P = Pa \qquad (4\text{-}2)$$

where $P$ is vapor pressure of solvent; and

$$\pi = (RT/V)a \qquad (4\text{-}3)$$

where $\pi$ is osmotic pressure of solution, and $V$ is molar volume of solvent. For ideal solutions the activity may be replaced by mole fraction, yielding the relationship.

$$a = \frac{\text{Mol. wt. solvent}}{\text{Wt. solvent}} \times \frac{\text{Wt. solute}}{\text{Mol. wt. solute}} \qquad (4\text{-}4)$$

Introducing this into the preceding equations places the molecular weight of the solute into the denominator of each expression. In other words, the measured changes in freezing point, vapor pressure, and osmotic pressure all decrease with increasing molecular weight of solute. This effect may be emphasized by comparing the colligative properties of

TABLE 4-1. Effect of Solute Molecular Weight on Colligative Properties of 1% Solution

|  | Molecular weight | |
|---|---|---|
|  | 100 | 100,000 |
| Freezing point depression ($\Delta T$), °C | 0.19 | 0.00019 |
| Boiling point elevation ($\Delta T$), °C | 0.05 | 0.00005 |
| Fractional vapor pressure change ($\Delta P/P$) | $1.8 \times 10^{-3}$ | $1.8 \times 10^{-6}$ |
| Osmotic pressure ($\pi$), cm of $H_2O$ | 2550 | 2.55 |

1%, by weight, aqueous solutions of compounds of molecular weights 100 and 100,000 (Table 4-1). Although an osmotic pressure value can be calculated for the lower molecular weight compound, in practice a semipermeable membrane for a molecule of only 100 molecular weight would be almost impossible to obtain. However, the other measurements are quite practical and frequently used in this molecular weight range. When the higher molecular weight material is considered, it is obvious that the first three methods are almost totally useless for experimental reasons. Only osmotic pressure is useful.

When making osmotic pressure measurements on polymer solutions, the calculated molecular weights are number averages (see Chapter 1). It has been found empirically that the molecular weights calculated from equation 4-3 are a function of concentration, primarily because the activity is a function of concentration. The data obtained may be represented by

$$\pi = cRT/\overline{M}_n + Ac^2 \qquad (4\text{-}5)$$

where $c$ is the concentration of the solute, of average molecular weight $\overline{M}_n$, in moles/liter. A plot of $\pi/RTc$ vs. $c$ yields a straight line such as shown in Figure 4-1, the intercept of which is $1/\overline{M}_n$. Equation 4-5 may be derived from statistical considerations of the polymer chains in solution. The slope of the plot, which is equal to $A$ of equation 4-5, is therefore of

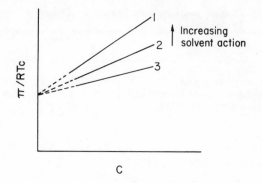

Figure 4-1. Osmotic pressure.

theoretical significance, and depends on the physics of the interaction between the solvent and the polymer chain. If the solvent used is a good solvent for the polymer (line 1, Fig. 4-1), there will be a strong interaction between the two and the plot will have a steep slope, making extrapolation to infinite dilution more difficult. For this reason, it is desirable to use a "poor" solvent (line 3, Fig. 4-1) in these measurements.

This apparent paradox, a poor solvent being a better choice, is dictated by the theory used to derive equation 4.5. In its simplest form this theory considers the polymer chain as an assemblage of points, on a latticework, which are tied together by chemical bonds. The polymer chain may assume any one of many statistically possible arrangements on the lattice, but interactions between different chains are not considered. Therefore the theory is most applicable for infinitely dilute solutions, and measurements at such concentrations are impossible to make. Hence it is necessary to extrapolate from finite concentration measurements to infinite dilution. At finite concentrations the polymeric chains become quite entangled and interactions between the chains can no longer be ignored. The development of an adequate solution theory to consider such real solutions is an area of continuing research.

**Fractionation.** If too poor a solvent is used, the polymer will not dissolve, of course. Conversely, if a polymer is dissolved in a good solvent and a very poor or nonsolvent is added to the solution, some polymer will precipitate. It has been found that the first polymer to precipitate will be of higher molecular weight than the number average molecular weight of the sample. This fact has been utilized to *fractionate* polymer samples and obtain subsamples having narrow molecular weight distributions. From these subsamples it is then possible to construct an *integral* molecular weight distribution curve as shown in Figure 4-2. The curve shown in Figure 1-2 is a *differential* distribution curve and may be constructed from the integral curve.

Fractionation may be carried out by a variety of methods either in a continuous or in a stepwise fashion. An example of the latter would be the simple procedure where a nonsolvent is slowly added at constant temperature to a solution of polymer in a good solvent. When turbidity appears, the addition is stopped and the two phases separated. It is

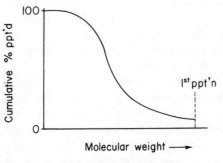

Figure 4-2. Fractional precipitation.

found that one phase is extremely polymer rich; this is considered to be the precipitated phase. The precipitated phase contains solvent, nonsolvent, and higher molecular weight polymer than that left in solution. The precipitated polymer may be dried and weighed. Further addition of nonsolvent to the solution will result in precipitation of ever lower molecular weight subsamples. Each of these samples after weighing may be subjected to molecular weight measurements, after which a graph such as Figure 4-2 may be constructed.

The simple procedure outlined above is quite tedious in practice, and elegant, continuous methods have been devised utilizing the same principles. In one such method solid polymer is placed at the top of a column of glass beads as shown in Figure 4-3. The upper portion of the column is heated, the lower cooled. At first pure nonsolvent is passed over the polymer. This is gradually enriched with a solvent. Only the lowest molecular weight material will go into solution at first, and this at an elevated temperature. When this first portion reaches the colder part of the column the polymer will be reprecipitated, there to stay until a more enriched solvent comes along. In this manner the material is continually dissolved and reprecipitated as it passes down the column, all the time being sorted out according to molecular weight, and the procedure has therefore been called precipitation chromatography. A fraction collector at the column exit automatically separates samples whose weight and molecular weight may then be determined.

Molecular weight distribution curves such as described above yield information about the kinetics of the reactions which produced the polymer chains. Such information in turn sheds light on the mechanisms and chemistry of polymerization reactions, leading to better and, hopefully, ultimate understanding and control of the processes. The attainment of such a goal is obviously desirable, and therefore

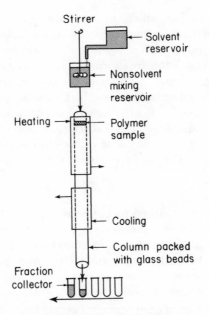

Figure 4-3. Column fractionation.

many routes toward it have been devised. For example, the exact shape of the distribution curve need not be completely determined, since one can tell a great deal about the distribution if only the number and weight averages are known. As detailed above, colligative properties yield number average molecular weights. Other measurements have been devised which are dependent on the weight average molecular weight of the sample.

*Light Scattering.* One of the most commonly used techniques for determining the weight average molecular weights of polymers is light scattering. This method, though highly sophisticated, rests on the 19th century work of Lord Rayleigh who showed that an ideal gas is not perfectly transparent to light, but rather has a turbidity—that is, the ability to scatter light—which depends on the polarizability of the gas, the wavelength of light, and the gas concentration. Einstein extended this treatment to liquids in 1910, by considering the thermal fluctuations in liquids which would cause optical inhomogeneities. In solutions, consideration must also be given to fluctuations in concentration. Because of these considerations, the theoretical expression for light scattering is related to that of osmotic pressure. For high polymers in solution, this expression takes the form:

$$Hc/\tau = 1/\overline{M}_w P(\theta) + 2Ac \qquad (4\text{-}6)$$

where $\tau$ is the measured turbidity at a particular angle, $\theta$, relative to the incident beam; $H$ is a constant for the system at a particular wavelength and concentration $c$; $P(\theta)$ is a function of the angle; $\overline{M}_w$ is the weight average molecular weight. The constant $A$ is the same as that which appeared in the osmotic pressure equation 4-5.

Measurements of light scattered by polymer solutions are complicated experimentally by background scattering which must be reduced to a minimum—ideally, to the scattering of the pure solvent. This minimum can be attained only by a filtration in order to remove all dust particles. The experiments are further complicated by the facts that equation 4-6 applies only for dilute solutions and that it contains a term, $P(\theta)$, which is dependent on the shape of the molecules in solution. These two facts necessitate a double extrapolation, one to infinite dilution, as in osmotic pressure, and the other to zero angle where the term $P(\theta)$ has the value unity. Such an extrapolation may be done graphically using a Zimm plot as shown in Figure 4-4. In this plot $k$ is an arbitrary constant.

From the zero angle–zero concentration intercept it is possible to calculate the weight average molecular weight. From

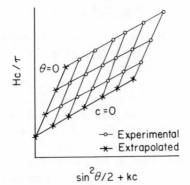

Figure 4-4. Light scattering.

the slope of the zero angle line, the value of $A$ in equation 4-6 may be calculated. As pointed out above; this is a measure of the polymer-solvent interaction, and quite useful to the study of solution thermodynamics. From the slope of the zero concentration line the average radius of gyration of the polymer chains in solution may be calculated. So it may be seen that the information available from this sophisticated technique is well worth the effort.

*Intrinsic Viscosity.* Detailed discussions of other methods of molecular weight determination may be found in more advanced texts. There is, however, a method which is so useful and generally applied that it must be considered in any first discussion. This method takes advantage of the fact that the *intrinsic* viscosity, $[\eta]$, of an infinitely dilute polymer solution is related to the number average molecular weight by the equation:

$$[\eta] = K(\overline{M}_n)^\alpha \tag{4-7}$$

where $K$ and $\alpha$ are constants for a particular polymer-solvent system at a given temperature. The specific viscosity, $\eta_{sp}$, may be measured in a viscometer by means of the relation:

$$\eta_{sp} = t/t' - 1 \qquad (4\text{-}8)$$

where $t$ is the flow time of a solution of concentration $c$, and $t'$ is the flow time of the pure solvent. A plot of $\eta_{sp}/c$ vs. $c$ yields a straight line the intercept of which is $[\eta]$. Equation 4-7 is essentially a calibration equation, which requires that $\overline{M}_n$ must be determined on a series of samples by a technique such as osmotic pressure and the intrinsic viscosity of each sample then determined. Once this has been done, the determination of polymer molecular weights becomes a simple, routine procedure, suitable for a control laboratory.

*End Group Analysis.*   All of the above methods have a dual utility; they serve as an analytical tool for the measurement of molecular weight and also yield information which is invaluable in evaluating theories of solution behavior of polymers. Because of this dual nature, these methods are all subject to the uncertainties of their underlying theories. This is undesirable from an analytical viewpoint. For this reason absolute analytical methods for the determination of molecular weights have been devised which depend on end group analysis.

It will be recalled that in condensation polymerization the number of unreacted functional groups is proportional to the molecular weight. In addition polymerization each chain must contain an initiator fragment (unless it has been started by chain transfer), and if termination is by combination, there will be two initiator fragments for each polymeric chain. These facts immediately suggest that if one could determine the mole fraction of chain ends by measuring the concentration of unreacted functional groups in condensation, or initiator fragments in addition polymerization, one would have an absolute determination of molecular weight. Although simple in concept, this suggestion is sometimes quite difficult to apply. The difficulties encountered fall into three general categories.

1. A high polymer having a degree of polymerization of 1000 will have only two end groups; if the polymer is placed in solution for analysis at a concentration of, say, 5%, the concentration of end groups will be only 100 parts per million. Such a concentration requires extremely sensitive analytical procedures.

2. In preparing the sample for analysis, degradation of the polymer chain or loss of very low or very high molecular weight chains must be avoided.

3. The number of functional end groups or initiator fragments per chain must be known. If extensive branching of the chain, chain transfer, or termination by unknown mechanisms has occurred, it will not be possible to assign a molecular weight with any high degree of precision. In this case, a physical measurement of the molecular weight would be more desirable.

In spite of these restrictions, end group analysis has been successfully applied in many instances. For example, the concentrations of unreacted amino end groups in polyamides have been determined by a very sensitive potentiometric procedure. The polymer is dissolved in *m*-cresol and titrated to a potentiometric end point by the addition of a methanolic solution of perchloric acid. Another procedure involves the use of benzoyl peroxide containing radioactive $C^{14}$ as an initiator in the polymerization of styrene. In this case styrene terminates exclusively by combination and the polymerizing chain undergoes very little transfer. The polymer is carefully isolated so as not to lose any low molecular weight material and then the radioactivity determined. If the specific activity of the initial benzoyl peroxide is known, it is a simple matter to determine the concentration of the fragments in the polymer, and thereby calculate the molecular weight.

*Thermodynamics of Polymer Solutions.* From the foregoing discussions it is possible to draw some general conclusions about the nature of polymers in solution. The most obvious fact about polymer solutions is that they are quite viscous, even at rather dilute concentrations. Quantitative considerations of the magnitude of the viscosity lead to the conclusion that the chains are quite flexible, and when present in sufficient concentration, their length and flexibility causes them to become entangled with one another. It is these entanglements which lead to the high viscosities.

A somewhat less obvious fact, but one which evolves from quantitative measurements, is that the heat of solution of many polymers in a variety of solvents is quite small. However, there is frequently a great deal of interaction between solvent and polymer, as measured by the parameter $A$ in equations 4-5 and 4-6. This interaction may therefore be almost totally ascribed to the change in entropy or degree of order upon mixing the long chain polymer molecules with the rather small solvent molecules. Statistical considerations of this entropy form the basis of theories of solution behavior, none of which are *totally* adequate because of approximations introduced into them, so as to render them tractable. In spite of this they do provide us with an insight and a beginning of quantitative explanations. For example, it is an experimental fact that most polymers will dissolve in poor solvents more readily at higher temperatures. The process of solution is dependent on the free energy change, $\Delta G$, accompanying it. This is given by the usual relation $\Delta G = \Delta H - T\Delta S$. Since the heat effect, $\Delta H$, is usually slightly positive, the process is governed primarily by the entropy effect, $\Delta S$. For the process to be thermodynamically possible, $\Delta G$ must be negative, and therefore $\Delta S$ must be positive. This is predicted by the statistical considerations previously mentioned. Increasing the temperature will increase the magnitude of the $T\Delta S$ term and result in a more thermodynamically favored process of solution.

All of the above discussion has dwelt on solutions whose concentrations are in a range of about 1% or less. As the solutions become more concentrated, polymer-solvent interactions cease to be the most important ones and attention must also be paid to polymer-polymer interactions. Such effects may be more easily approached through a discussion of the bulk polymers themselves without any solvent present.

### Bulk Properties

The properties of "plastic" materials are familiar to all and encompass quite a range of behavior. Polyethylene is semirigid and flexible; polystyrene is almost inflexible and rather brittle; rubber is quite flexible and not at all brittle. These are the properties as observed under ordinary temperatures; but subject rubber to temperatures of $-40°$ or $-50°$, or polystyrene to boiling water, and different adjectives would be required to describe their mechanical behavior. The problem of which adjective to use can be circumvented by defining a quantitative measure of mechanical behavior, known as a modulus and given the symbol $E$, $G$, or $B$, depending on whether we are discussing the mechanical behavior under tension, shear, or compression. In all cases the modulus is defined as the ratio of the applied stress to the resultant strain.

For an ideally elastic substance the modulus of elasticity may be measured quite simply by applying a tensile stress to a specimen and measuring the fractional change in length (strain). With a polymeric sample the calculated modulus is found to be very dependent on the length of time involved in the measurements and on the temperature of the sample. Therefore it may readily be concluded that polymers are not ideally elastic substances. Nevertheless, the concept of a modulus is quite useful, but must be applied with care.

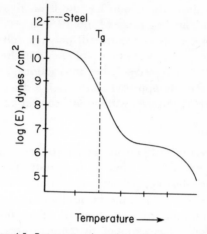

Figure 4-5. Temperature dependence of polymer elasticity.

Figure 4-5 shows graphically what our common experience indicates as the mechanical behavior of ordinary plastic materials. At low temperatures they are quite rigid and glassy, having a modulus of elasticity not too different from steel. As the temperature is raised, the modulus suddenly goes through a rapid change, or transitional region, in which the polymer has a leathery type of behavior. It is tough, but fairly flexible. This is called the glass transition region, and may be characterized by a single temperature, $T_g$. With further increase in temperature, the polymer becomes rubbery in quality. The "rubbery plateau" is characterized by a modulus, $E$, of about $10^7$ dynes/cm². If the polymer is heated beyond the rubbery state, it becomes molten and behaves like a very viscous liquid, losing all structural rigidity.

The temperature range necessary for quantitative observation of these four distinct types of behavior may be quite large if all measurements are made by exactly the same tech-

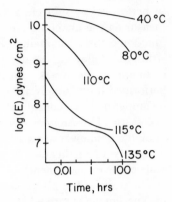

Figure 4-6. Effect of temperature on modulus of polymethylmethacrylate.

nique. It was pointed out above that the measured modulus is a function of time *and* temperature, and this fact may be used to observe all regions. In Figure 4-6 are shown plots of measurements of $E$ for polymethylmethacrylate at a variety of temperatures as a function of time. Note that the time scale is logarithmic, and consider the task of the experimenter trying to obtain data which will yield equally spaced points on such a plot: the necessary time intervals might be after 1, 10, and 100 seconds, providing a hectic beginning to the experiment. The next reading might be 1000 seconds, allowing time for a quick coffee break. This will be followed by a period of 10,000 seconds which makes for a fairly leisurely afternoon. The problems of working in logarithmic time are thus seen to be quite different from those in linear time. It is fortunate, then, that the effects of time and temperature may be superimposed so that data may be gathered over a reasonable temperature interval without undue haste or excessive leisure.

Experiments which yield data such as those in Figure 4-6 are known as *creep* or *stress relaxation* experiments. They may be performed by subjecting a sample to a constant load and measuring the changing strain or creep of the sample as a function of time, or maintaining a constant deformation or strain and following the decreasing amount of stress needed to maintain the strain. Either type of experiment may be performed quite simply in a crude fashion, but, to obtain meaningful data, considerable refinement of technique is necessary. This refinement has sometimes taken the form of applying a time-variant load to the sample, in which case the frequency of application of the load determines the time scale of the measurement.

The study of the phenomena involved in the various types of experiments is termed *rheology*, which means the study of flow. It is a particularly appropriate name since not only is the macroscopic flow of polymeric materials studied, but the microscopic interpretation of the observations is based on the flow of molecules past one another. In the glassy region, modulus is almost time-independent, which is to say that there is no flow. The molecules are constrained by weak, short-range forces due to dipole interactions as mentioned in Chapter 1. These forces are too small to maintain most low molecular weight substances in a solid state, but the magnitude of the force *per molecule* becomes very great for high polymers. This results in the glassy state. As the polymer is warmed, it achieves sufficient kinetic energy to overcome a portion of these short-range forces and enters into the transition region, where short-range motions of segments of the polymer chains are possible. Ultimately, if the polymer is warmed enough, all the short-range forces will be overcome. The only constraint then placed upon the polymer is that of the chain entanglements. That these entanglements can hold the whole collection of chains together for fairly long time periods is readily apparent to anyone who has tried to untangle a snarled fishing line. But, just as the fishing line ultimately can be untangled, so, too, given time, can the polymer chains slide past one another and loose their entanglements. Since it is essentially a kinetic problem of the chains, it can be solved either by allowing them time or by giving them more kinetic energy, that is, raising the temperature. Thus the superposition of time and temperature effects mentioned above is seen to have a simple molecular explanation. Once the chains have slipped their entanglements, flow of the polymer mass is analogous to that of a liquid. The extreme lengths of the molecules make this flow viscous.

With this qualitative molecular interpretation of the rheological behavior of polymers as a background it is possible to consider two further aspects: a mathematical model capable of quantitatively describing the flow processes, and an explanation of the behavior based on the chemical nature of the polymers involved.

*Mathematical Description.* One model commonly used in mathematically interpreting the flow behavior of polymers is the Voigt model, which consists of an ideally elastic spring connected in parallel with a dashpot. The dashpot is a piston and cylinder which contains a Newtonian liquid. The application of a stress to the system, as shown in Figure 4.7$A$, will induce a strain. The viscous dashpot will respond more slowly than the spring, in effect damping the over-all response of the system. This is described quantitatively by the equation

$$\eta \, ds/dt + E \times s = f \tag{4-9}$$

where $\eta$ is the viscosity of the dashpot; $E$ is the elastic modulus of the spring; $f$ is the applied stress; and $ds/dt$ is the time rate of change of the strain, $s$. If equation 4-9 is integrated, we can obtain

$$s = (f/E)[1 - \exp(-t/\tau)] \tag{4-10}$$

where $\tau$ is the ratio $\eta/E$ and has the units of time. For this reason $\tau$ is called the *relaxation time* of the Voigt element. Although, not even the simplest polymer system can be described in terms of one Voigt element, it is possible to describe many systems reasonably well by considering a generalized Voigt model where a large number of single Voigt elements are connected in series. Each element is characterized by its own relaxation time, and the polymer which is represented by the generalized model is said to have a spectrum of relaxation times.

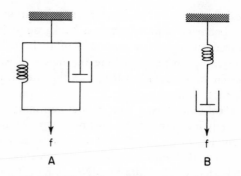

A                                    B

Figure 4-7. Voigt (A) and Maxwell (B) models of elastic behavior.

It is of interest to consider further that such a mechanical model is capable of describing the tangled mass of giant molecules we have envisioned. Actually the model is not complete enough to fully describe polymer behavior. While it can describe such properties as viscoelasticity and creep recovery quite well, it does not include properties such as instantaneous elastic response and flow, both of which are exhibited by many polymers. These two properties are readily accounted for by using a Maxwell element (Fig. 4-7*B*) in series with the Voigt element. Multiple combinations such as these, with a full spectrum of relaxation times, are then capable of explaining why, for example, the glass transition region is spread over such a large time (or temperature) range.

*Chemical Explanation of Rheological Behavior.* The many polymers whose syntheses were discussed in the earlier chapters all exhibit rheological phenomena such as those described above. It is important to remember that the phenomena are not at all observable under a single set of time-temperature conditions for all polymers. Polyisoprene is rubbery at room temperature; polystyrene is normally a glass below 80°C; polyethylene is predominantly crystalline up to about 130°C; and nylon 66 has a crystalline melting point of 235°C.

The ability of a polymer to be glassy, crystalline, or rubbery at a particular temperature must be regarded as an effect of the chemical makeup of the chain. If the polymer is primarily a hydrocarbon, the dispersion forces referred to in Chapter 1 will be of low magnitude, and an orientation of the polymer chains into the regular array characteristic of crystalline materials will only be possible if the chains themselves are quite regular. Bulky side groups or short-chain branches will detract from regularity and inhibit crystallization. On the other hand, if the chain includes polar atoms or groups of atoms, the strong interactions between these groups will tend to bring about crystallization. This tendency, of course, is opposed by the large, negative entropy change of crystallization. As a result, polymers such as the nylons crystallize quite readily and have high melting points, whereas polystyrene, which has the polar but bulky phenyl group, can be crystallized only under very special circumstances, and is normally glassy at room temperatures.

It must be recognized that the word "crystalline" as used in the above discussion does *not* carry exactly the same connotation as is attached to a crystal of sodium chloride or naphthalene; the nature of the crystalline state of polymers is still incompletely understood and must be regarded as a topic for future writings. However, a working idea of polymer crystallinity can be obtained if the long-chain molecules are considered to exist with each other in one of two states: the random or noncrystalline state is not unlike a bowl of cooked spaghetti, while the crystalline state consists of polymer chains which are regularly arranged with respect to each other, as in a bundle of uncooked spaghetti. With this analogy it is possible to conceive that a given polymer chain could pass in and out of crystalline and amorphous regions. The act of crystallization is then viewed as the process of bringing the "amorphous chains" together into "crystalline regions." It must be emphasized that this concept will in all probability be considerably refined by research presently in progress.

The glass transition temperature is also related to the chemical structure of the chain. The glassy state, unlike the crystalline state, is common to *all* polymers since it only requires a temperature low enough to restrict motion of the chains over a short distance, and does not require a long-range ordering of the chains. Therefore, the value of the transition temperature is also dependent on the polar nature of the chains. Table 4-2 lists glass transition temperatures and crystalline melting points of some polymers. Considera-

TABLE 4-2. Glass Transition $(T_g)$ and Melting $(T_m)$ Temperatures

| Polymer | $T_g$, °C | $T_m$, °C |
|---------|-----------|-----------|
| Polyisoprene | −73 | 11 |
| Polymethylacrylate | 3 | — |
| Polymethylmethacrylate | 65 | >200 |
| Polystyrene | 80 | 220 |
| Nylon 66 | 47 | 235 |
| Polyvinyl chloride | 70 | 140 |

tion of the various values in the light of the chemical composition of the substances will serve to emphasize the points made in the preceding paragraphs.

When the polymer chains are chemically bonded to one another through *cross-links*, the rheological behavior is affected markedly. As a result of cross-linking, the many chains become, in fact, one chain. Motion of chain segments is possible, but the sliding of one chain past another and loosening of entanglements are no longer possible. As a result the rubbery state persists over a greater temperature range and *elasticity* is imparted to the sample. Cross-links can be introduced into polymers by the use of trifunctional monomers in condensation polymerizations or by the use of dienes in vinyl polymerizations. Natural rubber is polyisoprene, and the residual double bond in each monomer unit incorporated into the chain presents a site for cross-linking.

The basic equation of rubber elasticity considers the effect of cross-links on the force, $f$, required to stretch rubber of length $l_0$ to length $l$.

$$f = (dRT/M)[l/l_0 - 1/(l/l_0)^2] \qquad (4\text{-}11)$$

where $d$ is the density of the rubber; $R$ is the gas constant; and $M$ is the molecular weight between cross-links. As the number of cross-links increases, $M$ will decrease and the force required to produce a given extension of the rubber must increase. If a very large number of cross-links is incorporated into the polymer, it ceases to be elastic. The polymer is no longer *thermoplastic*, but now becomes *thermosetting*.

Although polymers can be obtained with an immense variety of physical properties, it is not always possible to find in a single polymer the combination of ideal physical and chemical behavior and low cost which a particular application requires. For this reason, copolymerization has become a common method of modifying polymer properties. For example, polybutadiene, which has the rather low glass transition temperature of $-70°C$, can be copolymerized with styrene in an equimolar ratio to produce a rubber with a transition temperature of $-45°C$ which is more useful in higher temperature applications. When ethylene or propylene is homopolymerized, a crystalline polymer results; but copolymerization of the two destroys the crystallinity because of the randomness along the chain, and the copolymer makes an excellent rubber after cross-linking.

In addition to changing the rheological behavior, copolymerization can effect changes in such properties as: resistance to solvent attack, the ease of dyeing or printing on a polymer, and electrical insulation. In all these cases, the choice of comonomer can be made on the basis of the chemical properties of the monomer and the desired physical properties. The exact composition of the final copolymer is usually determined empirically.

### Textile Fibers

One of the largest uses of polymeric materials is as textile fibers. The physical requirements which a polymer must meet in order to be an economically useful fiber include ease of manufacture as a fiber; dyeability; stability to light, heat, and moisture; and a high tensile strength. The extent to which all but the last of these requirements are fulfilled is essentially determined by the chemical characteristics of the chosen polymer. However, the tensile strength of most polymers can be greatly increased by mechanical action alone.

That this should be possible is readily understood in the light of what has been said about the nature of the amorphous state of polymers and the weak attractive forces acting between them. It will be recalled that a tensile force on an amorphous polymer ultimately causes the chains to slide past one another. In doing this, though, the chains will tend to align themselves with one another. Where the spatial considerations allow it, crystallization will then occur. But, even if crystallization is not possible, the net result will be to place the chains in a more orderly arrangement with respect to each other and thereby permit greater interaction of the dispersion forces—dipole-dipole interactions, etc.—between them. The process which achieves this is known as *drawing* and is of the greatest importance to the production of textile fibers.

In the course of the drawing process the polymer sample will increase in length and decrease in cross-sectional area as shown in Figure 4-8. As a result, the tensile strength, defined as the ratio of force to cross-sectional area, increases greatly up to the ultimate point of rupture. The polymer may or may not crystallize, but it will be oriented and therefore have greatly increased tensile strength.

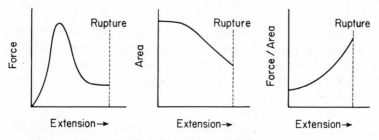

Figure 4-8. Effect of stretching on textile fibers.

## Diffusion in Polymers

One final aspect of the bulk behavior of polymers which deserves mention because of its technological importance is the subject of diffusion of gases and vapors through polymer films. The importance rests on the fact that polymer films have come to be extensively employed as wrapping materials for foods and manufactured goods. In almost all cases, one reason for the use of the wrapping is to protect the object from contamination by a component of the atmosphere—oxygen, moisture, carbon dioxide, or some other minor constituent of the air we breathe.

For a gas to pass through a polymer film, it must first dissolve in the outer layer of the film. The process of *permeation* is then a combination of solution followed by diffusion. This can be expressed mathematically as

$$P = DS \qquad (4\text{-}12)$$

where $P$ is the rate constant for permeation; $D$ is the Fick's law diffusion constant; and $S$ is the Henry's law constant relating solubility to vapor pressure. Each of these three constants displays an exponential temperature dependence of the form

$$D = D_0 \exp\,(-E_D/RT) \qquad (4\text{-}13)$$

where $D_0$ is a constant; $E_D$ is an energy term; $R$ is the gas constant; and $T$ is absolute temperature. Experimental verification of equation 4-13 for many polymer systems has led to the development of the idea of *activated* diffusion. According to this idea, the segmental motion of polymer chains develops void spaces in the film. When one of these spaces appears adjacent to a dissolved gas molecule, the molecule can then move into the void, leaving another space behind it. The net direction of motion for all the dissolved gas molecules is decided by the existence of a concentration gradient. Diffusion then consists of gas molecules moving in one direction, while void spaces are effectively moving in the other. It is termed "activated" diffusion because the chains must be activated by thermal energy, $E_D$, to cooperatively form the void spaces necessary for the motion of the dissolved gas molecules.

For many polymers the permeation process described above is not valid since either Fick's or Henry's law is not obeyed. This is particularly true in polymer–water vapor systems where hydrogen bonding occurs between the water molecules and polar groups on the polymer chain. In such a case, the application of physico-chemical adsorption theories is necessary to explain existing data.

_____

# chapter five

# STEREOCHEMISTRY
# OF POLYMERS

It is unfortunately possible to learn a great deal of chemistry without ever considering the fact that molecules exist in three-dimensional space, and that much of what is important must take this fact into consideration. As an example of this, all the formulas for the polymer molecules which have been written in this book up to this point are only two-dimensional. Obviously, this is a restriction imposed by the nature of printer's ink and paper. Not as obvious, though, is its effect on our consideration of everything about the nature of polymers and their behavior. In this chapter attention will finally be paid to what is perhaps the most important aspect of the nature of polymers.

As a first step it is necessary to adopt a convention for representing the three dimensions in only two. Since most of the polymers which will be discussed have primarily carbon atom chains, the tetrahedral carbon atom will be shown in the usual *planar projection*. When this is not adequate, bonds coming out of the plane of the paper will be shown by a heavy line and bonds behind the plane of the paper by a dashed line, as in Figure 5-1 C.

It is also necessary to consider the spatial relationships be-

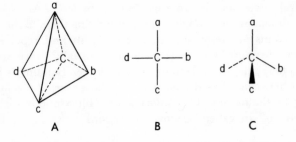

Figure 5-1. A, Tetrahedral carbon atom. B, Planar projection. C, d behind plane of page, c in front of plane of page.

tween the groups on adjacent carbon atoms. To do this, imagine that you are looking along the axis of the carbon–carbon single bond. The groups attached to the foremost carbon atom (a, b, and c in Fig. 5-2) will be displayed in an equilateral triangle while the rear groups (d, e, and f) will form another triangle. The angle between one group and its nearest neighbor on the other atom is called the di-

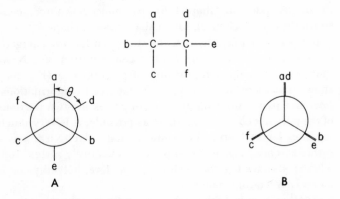

Figure 5-2. In the staggered form (A), the dihedral angle, $\theta = 60°$. In the eclipsed (B), $\theta = 0°$.

hedral angle, and it can vary from 0 to 60°. At 60° the substituent groups and the electrons binding them to the carbon atoms are least able to interact with and repel each other; therefore the staggered form is usually more stable than the eclipsed. In certain cases hydrogen bonding is possible between eclipsed groups, and in these cases the eclipsed may be the more stable conformation. Illustrations such as Figure 5-2 are called Newman projections.

## Rotation and Conformation

Whichever is the more stable form, conversion between the various possibilities is assured by free rotation about the carbon–carbon single bond. The word "free" is used in connection with rotation even though there may be small energy barriers (of the order of 1 kcal/mole) which must be surmounted as a given angle between two groups is varied through the total of 360°. It is this free rotation which permits a polymer molecule to exist in a more or less random coil. If free rotation were not possible, the molecule might exist as a rigid rod. In certain cases, particularly proteins (to be discussed in Chapter 6), *intra*molecular forces constrain the coil to a helical, rather than random shape.

In the case of polyethylene, the staggered form is energetically favored over the eclipsed, but consideration of a Newman projection of the repeat unit of polyethylene (Fig. 5-3) shows that there are two types of staggered conformations, *trans* and *skew*. Since the trans form places the two portions of the polymer chain as far apart as possible, it is very much the more favored form. The result is that polyethylene has a rather extended zigzag chain which is effectively a rigid rod. These rods pack together well and, therefore, polyethylene is a highly crystalline material.

Another simple hydrocarbon polymer is polyisobutylene. The proportion of carbon and hydrogen in polyisobutylene is

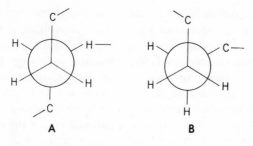

Figure 5-3. Trans (A) and skew (B) forms of poly-ethylene, $-(CH_2CH_2)_n-$.

almost the same as that in polyethylene, and yet the former is a rubber at room temperature, while the latter is crystal-line. Why? The answer rests in the stereochemistry of poly-isobutylene, shown as Newman projections in Figure 5-4. Unlike polyethylene, which has only hydrogen atoms on the chain backbone, polyisobutylene has two methyl groups on alternate carbon atoms. As a consequence, the trans form is not energetically different from the skew. Therefore in

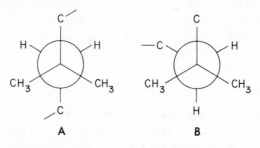

Figure 5-4. Trans (A) and skew (B) forms of polyiso-butylene, $-(CH_2\overset{\overset{\displaystyle CH_3}{|}}{\underset{\underset{\displaystyle CH_3}{|}}{C}})_n-$.

passing from one atom to the other along the chain, trans and skew conformations will be encountered in a random fashion. The chain itself will then be found to have an equally random, coiled shape. Because the energy barriers to rotation from the trans to the skew conformation are small, the presence of thermal energy will cause the chain segments to rotate continually with respect to one another. With respect to the entire chain this will create the effect of its writhing like a tortured snake. A collection of such molecules will entangle one another quite rapidly and form a viscoelastic mass—in short, a rubber. As pointed out in Chapter 4, it is necessary to introduce cross-links between the chains if a useful rubber is to be obtained. Otherwise a tensile force on the chains will separate their entanglements so much that the macroscopic sample will rupture.

It is of interest to note that polymethylmethacrylate, which does not become rubbery until well over 100°C, presents the same stereochemical picture as does polyisobutylene. However, polymethylmethacrylate contains the polar carboxyl group, which provides for strong interactions between various chain segments. This, then, demands that more thermal energy be supplied to permit rotation about bonds and writhing of chains. The physical consequence is that polymethylmethacrylate is a glass at the same temperature at which polyisobutylene is a rubber.

### Isomerism

When a conjugated diene such as isoprene or butadiene is polymerized, each repeating unit will contain a double bond. Four types of additions are possible, and the configurations which result are illustrated in Figure 5-5 for polyisoprene. If the polymerization takes place so that the 1,2 or the 3,4 double bond is used, then there will be a pendant double bond on the chain. If the addition of the monomer to the

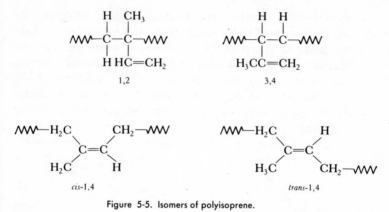

Figure 5-5. Isomers of polyisoprene.

growing chain is a 1,4 addition, then the residual double bond will be in the chain backbone and *cis-trans* isomerism about the double bond becomes possible. The polyisoprene which is isolated from the rubber tree, *Hevea brasiliensis*, has an all *cis*-1,4 structure. The polyisoprene produced as synthetic rubber by free radical polymerization has a structure which is a mixture of 1,2 and 3,4 and some *trans*-1,4, but no *cis*-1,4. This difference in stereochemistry is quite important, for the free radical polyisoprene does not have the same physical properties as the natural rubber and is inferior to it in most respects.

Another type of stereochemical difference which is possible when vinyl monomers are polymerized is *d,l* isomerism. Such isomerism is best visualized by inspection of Figure 5-1*C*. If any two substituents, say a and c, are interchanged, the resultant tetrahedron will then be a mirror image of the first one and nonsuperimposable upon it. Because of the lack of symmetry, polarized light will be rotated in different directions by the two different tetrahedra. These directions are *d*extro (right) and *l*evo (left), hence the name:

*d,l* isomerism. Carbon atoms containing four different substituents are said to be asymmetric. If a *molecule* is to rotate the plane of polarized light the whole molecule must be asymmetric. The lack of symmetry may be due to the presence of an asymmetric atom or may be a property of the molecule as a whole. Conversely, the presence of asymmetric atoms does not guarantee the asymmetry of the molecule.

In vinyl polymers such as polystyrene (5-1), every other

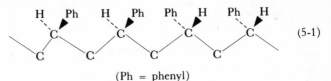

$$(5\text{-}1)$$

(Ph = phenyl)

carbon atom is asymmetric. Note that the hydrogens have been omitted from the nonasymmetric atoms for clarity. The first two asymmetric atoms have a different configuration than the last two. This chain could be represented for stereochemical purposes as

$$-d-d-l-l- \qquad (5\text{-}2)$$

A nomenclature has been adopted to describe stereochemical sequences with respect to the tacticity or placement of the asymmetric atoms in the chain. If the chain placements are always the same as the preceding one,

$$-d-d-d-d-d- \qquad or \qquad -l-l-l-l- \qquad (5\text{-}3)$$

then the sequence is said to be *isotactic*. If the placements are strictly alternating *d* and *l*

$$-d-l-d-l-d-l- \qquad (5\text{-}4)$$

then the sequence is said to be *syndiotactic*.

Completely random placements of *d* and *l* configurations

are recognized, and are called *atactic*. If an atactic chain is inspected, it is seen to be a collection of isotactic and syndiotactic runs of varying length.

$$-d-l-d-d-d-d-l-l-d-l-d-l-l-l-l-l-d-d-d-l-d-d-l-d- \quad (5\text{-}5)$$

That tacticity, or the lack of it, has an important bearing on the physical properties of polymers has only come to be fully appreciated within the past decade. If a polymer has bulky side groups, such as the phenyl group in polystyrene, then the packing requirements of crystallinity can only be satisfied if there is a stereochemical regularity to the chains. That is, the chains can only crystallize if there are long runs of iso- or syndiotactic placements.

### Stereospecific Polymerization

Prior to 1955, virtually all addition polymerizations were performed with no regard to the tacticity of the resultant polymer (the word "tacticity" itself had not even been coined). The synthesis of "natural" rubber could be conceived, but not achieved. Synthetic rubbers were, in some cases, poor compromises between ideality and technological ability. Vinyl polymers were almost always produced by free radical polymerizations, which, it has since been found, offer little or no chance for producing stereoregular polymers. Polyethylene was polymerized only via free radicals, and expensive high pressure processes were required.

Such was the situation when almost simultaneous developments in the laboratories of Dr. Karl Ziegler in Germany, Dr. Giulio Natta in Italy, the rubber and oil companies and several universities in the United States gave rise to what has rightly been called a "revolution in polymer chemistry." Quite simply, the revolution consisted of recognizing and gaining control of the stereochemistry of the propagation step in polymerization.

To trace developments leading to stereospecific polymerization, and to give credit where credit is due, has become the task of the patent attorneys and the courts because of the economic significance which always seems to be attached to polymer chemistry. Therefore, the rest of this chapter will only sketch the results of an enormous research labor on the part of many polymer chemists.

*Controlled Propagation.*   When a propagating vinyl polymer chain adds a monomer, the asymmetric carbon in the added monomer unit can be the same as the one in the previous unit or it can be of the opposite configuration. As defined above, these are respectively isotactic and syndiotactic placements.   For either of the reactions 5-6 to be

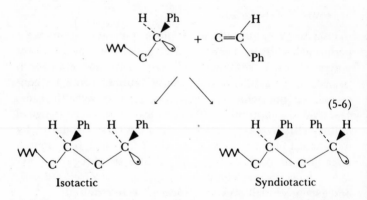

(5-6)

Isotactic                                     Syndiotactic

achieved, the reactants must pass through an activated complex.   There will be a free energy change, $\Delta G^*$, accompanying the change from reactants to activated complex. The rate constants for the isotactic and syndiotactic reactions can be written as

$$k_{iso} = (RT/\mathbf{N}h) \exp (-\Delta G^*_{iso}/RT)$$

$$k_{syn} = (RT/\mathbf{N}h) \exp (-\Delta G^*_{syn}/RT)$$

(5-7)

where $R$ is the gas constant; **N** is Avogadro's number; **h** is Planck's constant; and $T$ is absolute temperature. If there is no difference between the two free energies of activation, iso-tactic and syndiotactic placements will occur randomly, and the polymer chain will be atactic. On the other hand, if there is a free energy difference of as little as 2 kcal/mole in favor of one of the placements, that one will occur more than 95% of the time at room temperature; 4 kcal/mole gives a 99.9% favoring. The resultant polymer chain will then have a steric regularity which permits crystallization to occur. Similar considerations about free energies of activation apply to diene polymerizations where 1,2 or 3,4 or *cis-* or *trans*-1,4 additions are possible.

Since the energy difference required to favor one form over the other is so small, it is surprising that there is so little stereoregularity to many polymerizations. This must be a consequence of the small differences in interactions in the transition states. However, it has been found that certain types of vinyl polymerizations exhibit a great deal of stereo-regularity in the polymer chain which is presumably due to steric or energetic effects in the transition state. Most of these polymerizations are ionic in character, and the discus-sion of them was not included in Chapter 2, so that they might be considered in the light of their stereochemistry.

### Cationic Polymerization

The first stereospecific vinyl polymerization to be clearly recognized as such was that of isobutyl vinyl ether with boron trifluoride etherate as an initiator. Boron trifluoride initiator is a strong Lewis acid, and the polymerization is therefore recognized as proceeding via a cationic propaga-tion mechanism.

For a polymerization to proceed cationically, it must first be initiated by a Lewis acid. In many cases, the actual initiating acid is the product of a reaction between a catalyst and cocatalyst, for example, equation 5-8. In this instance,

$$AlCl_3 + H_2O \rightarrow [Cl\underset{\underset{Cl}{|}}{\overset{\overset{Cl}{|}}{Al}}OH]^- H^+ \quad (5\text{-}8)$$

the Lewis acid, aluminum chloride, reacts with a trace of moisture to give a proton plus a complex negative ion. The proton then initiates the polymerization. The negative ion, which had been associated with the proton, then becomes associated with the positive carbonium ion which is at the propagating end of the chain. The initiation of isobutylene polymerization is given in 5-9 as an illustration. Polymeriza-

$$[AlCl_3OH]^- H^+ + CH_2=C(CH_3)_2 \rightarrow$$

$$[AlCl_3OH]^- + CH_3\underset{\underset{CH_3}{|}}{\overset{\overset{CH_3}{|}}{C}}{}^+ \quad (5\text{-}9)$$

tion proceeds by addition of the carbonium ion chain end to the double bond of a monomer. Termination of the polymerization can occur by a reaction such as 5-10.

$$\text{\textapprox\textapprox}-CH_2\underset{\underset{CH_3}{|}}{\overset{\overset{CH_3}{|}}{C}}{}^+ [AlCl_3OH]^- \rightarrow$$

$$\text{\textapprox\textapprox}-CH_2\underset{\underset{CH_3}{|}}{\overset{\overset{CH_2}{\|}}{C}} + [AlCl_3OH]^- H^+ \quad (5\text{-}10)$$

It is interesting to note that although many monomers have been polymerized cationically, very little evidence of stereospecificity has been obtained this way since the first observations on isobutyl vinyl ether. The mechanisms by which cationic polymerizations are initiated and terminated are really quite diverse. Only one instance of each has been shown here. The reactions are also sensitive to traces of impurity, even more so than as emphasized in Chapter 1 for polymerizations in general. These facts when combined serve to explain, but do not justify, the over-all paucity of our detailed knowledge about cationic polymerization reactions.

### Anionic Polymerization

Just as cationic polymerization is propagated by carbonium ions, so anionic polymerization is propagated by carbanions. The initiation of polymerization requires moderately strong Lewis bases, such as $n$-butyllithium:

$$CH_3CH_2CH_2CH_2{}^-\text{---}Li^+ \; + \; H_2C{=}CHX \; \rightarrow$$

$$
\begin{array}{c}
\quad\quad\;\; H \\
\quad\quad\;\; | \\
H_3C(CH_2)_4C^-\text{---}Li^+ \; \xrightarrow{\;\;H_2C{=}CHX\;\;} \; \text{Polymerization} \quad (5\text{-}11) \\
\quad\quad\;\; | \\
\quad\quad\;\; X
\end{array}
$$

The carbon–lithium bond is intermediate between a simple ionic and a pure covalent bond, and has therefore been written as a dashed line with a charge on the atoms.

Unlike free radical or cationic polymerizations, there is no rapid termination reaction which can occur for the anionic chain ends. They are, however, very sensitive to the presence of trace impurities of Lewis acids such as water, carbon dioxide, or oxygen. If such reactants as these are rigorously excluded from anionic polymerization, the propagation will proceed until the monomer in the reaction mixture has been depleted. An analogy has been made between this behavior and that of an organism, the initiation being seen as birth, propagation as life, and termination as death. Since no termination mechanism was evident when these polymerizations were first studied, they were said to produce "living" polymers. Actually further study has shown that at high temperatures or after long time periods, termination does occur via a complex reaction path; so the "living" polymers are mortal after all.

There are two interesting consequences of the short-range immortality of these polymers. In the first place, it has proved possible to utilize their long life to reach equilibrium in vinyl polymerizations. As noted in Chapter 1, the free energy change, $\Delta G$, accompanying a polymerization is directly related to the monomer concentration present at equilibrium. Attainment of equilibrium is made experimentally very difficult when termination steps occur, but this is not so in anionic polymerizations. For example, in the polymerization of $\alpha$-methylstyrene (eq. 5-12) the

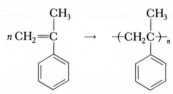

$$n\,CH_2=\underset{\underset{\displaystyle \bigcirc}{\overset{\displaystyle CH_3}{|}}}{C} \quad \rightarrow \quad \underset{\underset{\displaystyle \bigcirc}{\overset{\displaystyle CH_3}{|}}}{+CH_2C+_n} \qquad (5\text{-}12)$$

presence of two bulky side groups slows free radical propagation to almost a zero rate at low temperatures, and also brings about a low ceiling temperature. Polymerization is, therefore, thermodynamically impossible at high temperatures, and kinetically unreasonable at low temperatures. But anionic polymerization proceeds rapidly at low temperatures, and it is possible to polymerize $\alpha$-methylstyrene, with butyllithium as an initiator, and study the effect of temperature on the monomer-polymer equilibrium. Figure 5-6

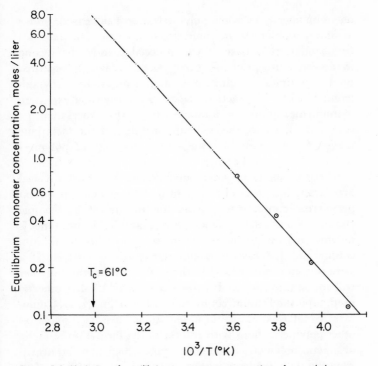

Figure 5-6. Variation of equilibrium monomer concentration of $\alpha$-methylstyrene with temperature.

presents the data from such a study. Note that the concentration of pure monomer is about $8M$, so polymerization cannot occur above 61°C. On the other hand, it is possible to get almost complete conversion of monomer to polymer only at very low temperatures. Studies such as this are continuing to shed light on the thermodynamics of polymerization processes.

Another interesting consequence of "living" polymers is the comparative ease with which block copolymers may be produced using them. All that is necessary is to polymerize one monomer, and, when polymerization has ceased, add a second monomer. If the chain end of the first monomer is a sufficiently strong base, it will proceed to add the second monomer. In principle this process may be repeated numerous times, yielding copolymers containing many different blocks. In practice, the need for rigorous exclusion of impurities limits the number of times the process can be repeated. Even so, the wide applicability of the technique makes it most useful for the "tailor-making" of polymers which was discussed earlier.

Stereospecificity in vinyl polymerizations which proceed anionically has been observed to be very dependent on experimental conditions such as the nature of the *positive* counterion and the solvent. For example, if isoprene is polymerized in a hydrocarbon solvent with a lithium counterion, the polymer is almost exclusively *cis*-1,4. If a sodium counterion is used in the same solvent, the polymer will contain no *cis*-1,4. If a solvent such as diethyl ether is used, even the lithium counterion will not give *cis*-1,4 polymer. Similar experimental observations have been made on other polymerizations with respect to the formation of tactic or atactic polymers. The conclusion which may be drawn from the data available is that the steric control (or the free energy favor, in terms of eq. 5-7) in the transition state is due to the nature of the carbon–metal bond. Since the study of organometallic compounds containing such bonds is relatively new and fraught with experimental difficulties, a more complete explanation of the steric control must await further work. In the meantime it will continue to be a fascinating problem for many research workers.

### Coordination Polymerization

In discussing the formation of inorganic polymers the term coordination polymerization was used to describe a type which was neither addition nor condensation. Unfortunately, the same term has also been used to describe organic addition polymerizations which are neither free radical nor simply ionic in their nature. Such polymerizations are encountered with the so-called Ziegler catalysts. These catalysts are combinations of organometallics such as triethylaluminum and transition metal compounds such as titanium tetrachloride. When these mixtures are prepared in the presence of a hydrocarbon solvent, a precipitate develops. It is impossible to state at this writing exactly how this precipitate brings about polymerization, but, from the experimental evidence so far obtained, a general idea of the mechanism can be deduced. In the first place, it is quite probable that the organometallic compound reduces the transition metal to a lower valence state producing, for example, in the reaction of triethylaluminum and $TiCl_4$, a molecule of diethylaluminum chloride, an ethyl free radical, and a molecule of $TiCl_3$:

$$(C_2H_5)_3Al \ + \ TiCl_4 \ \longrightarrow$$

$$(C_2H_5)_2AlCl \ + \ TiCl_3 \ + \ C_2H_5 \cdot \quad (5\text{-}13)$$

Further reduction to $TiCl_2$ is also possible. Since aluminum alkyls are electron-deficient compounds, complex formation between the lower valency titanium compounds and the aluminum alkyl can result in formation of the observed heterogeneous precipitate. One proposed mechanism suggests that complex 5-14 is responsible for the polymerization,

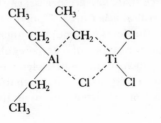

$$(5\text{-}14)$$

which proceeds as shown in equation 5-15.

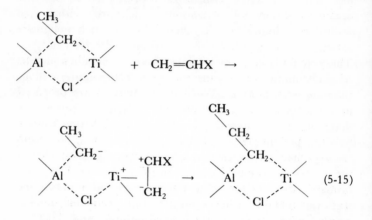

$$(5\text{-}15)$$

Thus the polymerization proceeds through what is essentially an anionic propagation, but one which occurs with much coordination between the chain end and the metal cation. Since this process is occurring on a heterogeneous surface, there is great steric control over the process. Actually, the presence of a macroscopic surface is not essential, since any three points define a plane or surface if they are fixed in space.

There are other mechanisms which have been proposed to explain Ziegler catalysis; some perhaps are better than the above. None, however, are so well substantiated as to engender confidence that they are necessarily true. This must be regarded as still another area of polymer research which is well worth the time of the careful investigator.

There is another type of stereoregular coordination polymerization which occurs when olefin oxides are mixed with ferric chloride (eq. 5-16). Note that in this reaction, there is an asymmetric carbon atom in the monomer. If

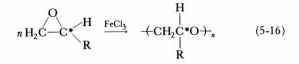

$$n \; H_2C \overset{O}{\underset{}{\diagup\!\!\diagdown}} C^* \overset{H}{\underset{R}{\diagdown}} \xrightarrow{FeCl_3} \; +\!(CH_2 \overset{H}{\underset{R}{C^*}} O)\!+_n \qquad (5\text{-}16)$$

the polymerization is stereoregulated, the configuration of that atom in the polymer can remain unchanged. If one starts with optically pure monomer (i.e., all $d$ or all $l$), the stereoregularly polymerized polymer will also be optically pure. The presence of the oxygen atom in the polymer chain means that the chain will not have a center of symmetry and the chain will therefore be optically active. This has been experimentally observed.

On the other hand, a vinyl polymer chain will have a center of symmetry, and, even though all of the asymmetric carbon atoms are in, say, a $d$ configuration, the chain will not have optical activity.

# THE POLYMERS
# OF NATURE

THE FOREGOING chapters have developed the principles of polymerizations as they occur in the laboratory and in manufacturing processes. They have also described to some extent the nature and behavior of these synthetically produced polymers. These principles and descriptions can be extended to include many of the polymeric substances which are found in living organisms. There is, however, a severe restriction on this last statement which is perhaps best exemplified by natural rubber, polyisoprene. This polymer can be made in the laboratory by polymerizing the compound isoprene. It is also made in the rubber tree, but there it is most definitely not made from monomeric isoprene. The reactions by which it is made in the tree involve metabolic processes too complex to be discussed here.

From the rubber tree, then, we can learn a lesson: polymerization in an organism is not the random process of addition or condensation which is observed in synthetic polymerization. Rather, it is a very controlled and directed process, the source of control residing in the metabolism of the organism itself. It is the lack of this control in the test tube which has frustrated most of the attempts to duplicate synthetically the polymers of living species. The measure of control over stereoregularity, discussed in the previous chapter, has rightly been regarded as a triumph of science. This triumph fades to an inconsequence when viewed in the light of the everyday syntheses of complex molecules by living organisms.

What, then, are some of the polymeric products of organisms? A complete list would demand another book, and the reader interested in a more thorough discussion of biochemical polymers is referred to the bibliography. Only a cursory description will be given here of a few polymers whose nature is well understood or, if not, whose organic functions are of immense importance.

### Polysaccharides

The very common substances sugar, starch and cellulose all belong to a class of compounds known as carbohydrates and have the empirical formula $C_x(H_2O)_y$. The ordinary table sugar, sucrose, is actually a dimeric compound formed from two simpler sugars, fructose and glucose. Glucose is also the main constituent of starch and cellulose, so an examination of this molecule's structure is in order. In 6-1

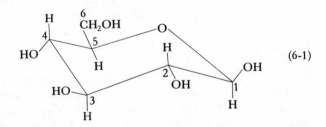

(6-1)

the glucose molecule is shown considerably puckered, in a chair conformation, with the attached atoms at tetrahedral angles to each other. Note that all five of the ring carbon atoms are asymmetric, and that the molecule as a whole is asymmetric. It has been found that two forms of glucose are common in nature, $\alpha$ and $\beta$, which differ only in the configuration about carbon atom 1.

Starch and cellulose are both polymers of glucose, with the chains being joined by ethereal oxygen links at the 1 and 4′ positions. In the amylose fraction of starch the configuration of the number 1 atom is $\alpha$ while in cellulose it is $\beta$. This is the only essential chemical difference between these two substances, but as a consequence of this single spatial interchange the two polymers have enormously different properties.

Starch can be hydrolyzed by body enzymes to $\alpha$-glucose, which is oxidized to carbon dioxide and water, yielding energy necessary for continuing bodily functions. Cellulose, on the other hand, defies hydrolysis by the body's enzymes and therefore cannot be utilized as food.

X-ray crystallography has revealed many of the details of the structural arrangement of starch and cellulose. Cellulose is believed to exist with fully extended chains which are bonded into a sheet structure by interchain hydrogen bonds. In the presence of water, these hydrogen bonds become disrupted by the water molecules which compete for hydrogen bonding sites. The same hydroxyl groups which are responsible for the hydrogen bonding are also susceptible to other reactions which lead to such products as rayon and cellulose acetate.

Starch molecules assume a helical conformation because the ethereal links joining the glucose molecules are on opposite sides of the ring. It is interesting to note that the resultant tubular molecule can accommodate iodine molecules inside itself, thus presenting a simple physical model for the well known starch-iodine complex.

## Proteins

Polyamides have been discussed in Chapter 2, the best known being nylon, a product of truly great research. Nature anticipated the genius of the synthetic chemists by many eons in the case of synthesizing polyamides. In every living cell there are polyamides, better known as *proteins*. They are synthesized by the organism from a group of twenty $\alpha$-amino acids (eq. 6-2), which are structually similar, differing only in the nature of the group, R, on the $\alpha$ carbon atom. Note that the carbon atom bearing the R

$$n\,NH_2\underset{\underset{H}{|}}{\overset{\overset{R}{|}}{C}}-\overset{\overset{O}{\|}}{C}OH \;\rightarrow\; +NH\underset{\underset{H}{|}}{\overset{\overset{R}{|}}{C}}-\overset{\overset{O}{\|}}{C}\!+_n \qquad (6\text{-}2)$$

group, which distinguishes the various $\alpha$-amino acids, is asymmetric. Most naturally occuring amino acids have the same configuration about this carbon atom, and this configuration is retained in the protein.

The polymerization indicated in equation 6-2 is actually a copolymerization, since in the resultant protein the many possible R groups occur along the chain in a sequence determined by the synthesizing organism. It is this peculiar ability of the organism, to determine sequence in a copolymerization of as many as twenty different monomers, which makes the achievements of the polymer chemist seem so small. Remember also that this is accomplished with an absolute retention of steric configuration.

The elucidation of the structures of the many, many proteins found in organisms is probably the most elusive and sought after knowledge in the world of chemistry today. One of the functions of these molecules in the body is as chemical catalysts, called enzymes. As such they bring about reactions which, though thermodynamically possible, are kinetically improbable at the relatively low temperatures at which organisms exist. For example, the conversion of $\alpha$-glucose to carbon dioxide and water, mentioned above, is an oxidation—more simply, a burning. We know that carbonaceous compounds do not burn unless we heat them to a very high temperature. This is not because oxidation is not possible but rather because the *rate* of burning is so slow at low temperatures. The bodily enzymes greatly speed this rate. In a similar fashion, other enzymes perform other tasks of catalysis.

The exact mechanisms of the various enzymic catalysts are not known. It has been proven, though, that there is complex formation between an enzyme and the reactant. It is also presumed that the rigorous stereochemistry and the particular sequence of amino acids found in a given protein enable it to operate in a very specific manner.

There is a third factor of protein structure which plays an important role in enzyme behavior, namely, the chain conformation. It has been found that many protein chains exist as helices. (Indeed, the presence of helical conformation in both natural and synthetic polymers of all sorts is so common that it is almost worthy of consideration as a separate state of matter.) Since the cells in which they exist are essentially an aqueous environment, it is not surprising that proteins present the polar portions of the chain on the outside of the helix, while burying the organic groups (the R groups) on the inside of the helix.

It is the purpose of current research to develop an understanding of the nature of the forces holding proteins in their helical conformation. Three principal forces have been recognized, although there is uncertainty as to their relative importance: electrostactic attractions, hydrogen bonding, and hydrophobic bonding. The first two terms are familiar, but the third needs some explanation. Since proteins exist in an aqueous environment, it is to be expected that the R groups of the various amino acids will be more stable in the interior of the helix where water may be excluded. Interactions between these hydrophobic groups can then serve to stabilize the helical conformation, hence the term, hydrophobic bond.

It must not be thought that all proteins are helical. Many are globular in shape. The detailed structure of one such protein, myoglobin, has been elucidated. It is found to consist of a continuous chain which loops and doubles back upon itself, thus presenting a rounded contour for its outline.

### Synthesis

Total synthesis of a given protein is not yet feasible in the laboratory. If the reaction is treated as the copolymerization of a number of amino acids, it is not possible to arrange their order in the chain. Rather, they will enter the chain in a random fashion. On the other hand, if the formation of the chain is treated via a stepwise process, introducing the amino acids in their proper order, then the number of necessary sequential reactions will be huge and the over-all yield miniscule.

In order to study the behavior of proteins it has proven valuable to synthesize polyamino acids from one amino acid at a time. The resultant homopolymer may then be studied with the entire spectrum of experimental techniques which has been developed for proteins. In a similar fashion, well-defined copolymers of two amino acids may be synthesized and studied. A common method for such polymerizations and copolymerizations is Leuch's anhydride synthesis, which employs an $N$-carboxy anhydride of the desired amino acid. A strong base, such as a primary amine, will attack the amine nitrogen and yield an amino amide and carbon dioxide (eq. 6-3). The amino group can then attack another anhydride and so propagate the polymer chain. Copolymerizations of such anhydrides can be described by reactivity ratios like those used for vinyl copolymerization in Chapter 2.

$$
\begin{array}{c}
\underset{|}{R} \quad \underset{\parallel}{O} \\
HC-C \\
\underset{|}{\phantom{HC}} \quad \phantom{C} \diagdown O \; + \; R'NH_2 \; \rightarrow \\
HN-C \\
\phantom{HN} \underset{\parallel}{\phantom{HN-C}} \\
\phantom{HN} O
\end{array}
\qquad
\begin{array}{c}
\phantom{R'} \quad \underset{\parallel}{O} \; \underset{|}{R} \\
R' \diagdown \\
\phantom{R'} \quad NC-CNH_2 \; + \; CO_2 \quad (6\text{-}3) \\
H \diagup \quad \underset{|}{\phantom{NC-C}} \\
\phantom{R' NC-C} H
\end{array}
$$

### Nucleic Acids

Having seen throughout the book the great diversity of polymers, the reader should not be surprised to learn that the very core of the life process, the genes themselves, are polymers. Indeed, it cannot be much of a surprise for anyone who reads a good newspaper. For the exciting discoveries of the past decade concerning nucleic acid make excellent copy for the science writers. As the "genetic code" is broken, the latest discoveries of biochemistry are transmitted to the general public. Since there has been so much of an elementary nature written about the nucleic acids, only the most fundamental chemical facts about their structure will be presented here.

The chain of a nucleic acid molecule is formed by the joining together of a large number of nucleotides to give a molecule having a molecular weight as high as tens of millions. Each nucleotide is composed of phosphoric acid, a sugar, and a base. All nucleic acids contain either D-ribose or D-2-deoxyribose as the sugar (6-4). Those containing ribose are known as ribonucleic acids (RNA) and those containing the other sugar are known as deoxyribonucleic acids

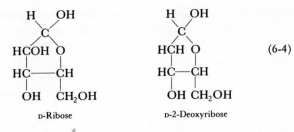

D-Ribose      D-2-Deoxyribose     (6-4)

(DNA). The bases found in the nucleotides are either purine or pyrimidine types. In DNA four bases are commonly found: thymine, adenine, guanine, and cytosine.

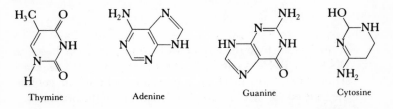

Thymine      Adenine      Guanine      Cytosine

A simple nucleotide might then have the structure shown in 6-5, where guanine is the base and deoxyribose the sugar.

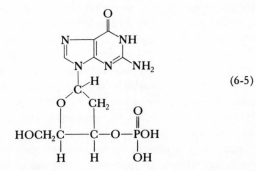

(6-5)

Such simple nucleotides have been polymerized in the laboratory, but only with the aid of enzymes. Totally "nonbiological" syntheses of polynucleotides must proceed in a stepwise fashion using blocking groups for the many functional groups which would interfere with the formation of linear polymers.

The linear polymer chain formed in nature has the structure 6-6, where the symbol "B" has been used to indicate one

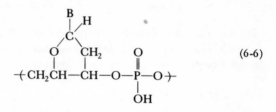

(6-6)

of the bases. Like the amino acids in proteins, the bases in DNA and RNA occur in a specific sequence. The exact sequence of bases in DNA is presently believed to contain the code which dictates the genetic pattern of the organism.

DNA is considered to exist as a two-stranded helix. That is, two DNA chains are wound about each other in a helical fashion, held together by hydrogen bonding between the bases. It has been shown that the spatial characteristics of thymine and adenine and guanine and cytosine make them ideal pairs for forming hydrogen bonds between two chains. Thus we can envision the DNA as consisting of a sequence of nucleotides, whose order is genetically determined, twisted into a helix which contains two chains. RNA is similar, but only has one chain. It is thought that DNA synthesizes itself and RNA by replication, that is, by a template mechanism of some sort. The RNA in turn is thought to synthesize protein chains by another template mechanism. Such hypotheses are appealing because of their basic simplicity and demand for rigorous control of stereochemistry. Both of these qualities are certainly characteristic of living systems, but actual details of these template mechanisms have not yet been elucidated and they must therefore be regarded as good working hypotheses.

## Conclusion

The detailed future of polymer chemistry cannot be foretold, but it is certain to include not only the production of better materials for technology, but also the better understanding of life processes. The achievement of goals such as these will require well-trained chemists with depth of imagination and breadth of knowledge. It is the sincere hope of the author that the reader will add to his knowledge and fire his imagination by turning to the bibliography and reading more about this extremely important area of chemistry.

# SELECTED READINGS

## General

Billmeyer, F. W., "Textbook of Polymer Science," Interscience, New York, 1962. An up-to-date general text, most useful for its many references.

Flory, P. J., "Principles of Polymer Chemistry," Cornell Univ. Press, Ithaca, N. Y., 1953. The classic book in this field. Chs. 1 and 2 are especially valuable as introductory reading.

*Journal of Chemical Education* **36,** April, 1959. A collection of papers on polymer chemistry of interest to teachers and students alike.

Melville, H., "Big Molecules," Macmillan, New York, 1958. An elementary book written in a very interesting way.

*Scientific American*, September, 1957. An entire issue devoted to polymers. Although some papers are now dated, all make excellent reading.

## Polymerization

Burlant, W., and A. Hoffman, "Block and Graft Copolymers," Reinhold, New York, 1960. Contains a wealth of experimental description.

Ham, G. (ed.), "Copolymerization," Interscience, New York, 1964. A complete survey of the subject.

"International Symposium on Inorganic Polymers (Nottingham, 1961)," Chemical Society, London, 1962. A collection of review papers by foremost researchers in this new area.

Stille, J. K., "Introduction to Polymer Chemistry," Wiley, New York, 1962. An excellent discussion of organic polymerization reactions in detail.

### Physical Properties

The following books give varied treatments of polymer physics and properties.

Bueche, F., "Physical Properties of Polymers," Interscience, New York, 1962.

Mark, H., and A. Tobolsky, "Physical Chemistry of Polymeric Systems," Interscience, New York, 1950.

Tanford, C., "Physical Chemistry of Macromolecules," Wiley, New York, 1961.

Tobolsky, A., "Properties and Structure of Polymers," Wiley, New York, 1960.

### Stereochemistry

Bawn, C., and A. Ledwith, *Quart. Revs.* **16,** 361 (1962). A review article on stereoregular addition polymerization.

Eliel, E., "Stereochemistry of Carbon Compounds," McGraw-Hill, New York, 1962. Chapter XV is especially pertinent to stereospecific polymerization.

Gaylord, N., and H. Mark, "Linear and Stereoregular Addition Polymers," Interscience, New York, 1959.

### Polymers of Nature

Alfrey, V., and A. Mirsky, "How Cells Make Molecules," *Scientific American*, September, 1961. A description of the replication process of DNA and RNA to produce proteins.

Fox, S., and J. Foster, "Protein Chemistry," Wiley, New York, 1957. A good introduction to the general subject of proteins.

Huggins, M. L., "Physical Chemistry of High Polymers," Wiley, New York, 1958, chs. 13 et seq. A description of structure with many references to other works.

Kendrew, J. C., *Science* **139,** 1259 (1962). An extremely interesting article detailing the research on the structure of myoglobin in particular and proteins in general.

# INDEX